Native Trees

Of The

Bahamas

by JACK PATTERSON

and GEORGE STEVENSON

*Dedicated to Byrle M. P., without whom
this book would never have been
written.*

ACKNOWLEDGEMENTS

The authors wish to thank the following; Dr. John Popenoe, PhD., Director of Fairchild Tropical Garden, for his help, support, and companionship, particularly when the field work was in progress; Dr. Donovan Correll, PhD., who is currently with Fairchild Tropical Garden and who is engaged in preparing a complete flora of the Bahamas, whose suggestions have been most helpful; Dr. William Gillis, PhD., whose interest and work in the Bahamas have been more than useful; Mr. George Avery, whose work in bringing the botanical names up to date has been invaluable; and last but not least, Messrs. Mike Lightbourn and Oris Russell, both long time members and past presidents of the Bahamas National Trust, whose individual support and companionship during the early days of writing and exploring were greatly appreciated.

HOPE TOWN
ABACO, BAHAMAS

INTRODUCTION

"The trees are as green and leafy as those of Castile in the months of April and May." So spake Christopher Columbus on landing at San Salvador.

The Bahamas is an archipelago, situated approximately between Latitude 21 and 27 degrees North and Longitude 73 and 79 degrees West. The axis runs nearly northwest to southeast and is about 600 miles long. There are about 700 islands and cays, not including numerous rocks. In most cases the land is low, but some of the islands and cays are quite hilly in places, with heights up to 200 feet.

The climate is considered subtropical, with temperatures rarely going above 90° F. in the summer and below 60° F. in the winter. Rainfall is moderate in the north; for example, most areas on Abaco record between 50 to 60 inches annually. This gradually becomes less as one proceeds south, with Inagua having an average of about 27 inches. Due to the proximity of large masses of water, humidity is relatively high, especially in the summer.

The Bahama Islands are composed wholly of aeolian limestone. There are no coral atolls, as in the Pacific, although the Hogsty Reef, north of Inagua, suggests one. However, there are fringing reefs to the east of most of the main islands. The best known is the one off Andros. Between some of the main islands there is considerable depth of ocean, in places falling off very steeply from the shallows. Some of the islands and cays are connected by shallow banks with a water depth of no more than ten fathoms, usually less.

The land is very rocky and on the coast it is common to have a narrow belt of very jagged rock. This is so pitted with holes by the action of the sea that it is known as honeycomb rock. It may make up the whole circumference of a particular island or cay. Attractive beaches of white sand are frequently encountered. Inland one sometimes finds sink-holes, known locally as potholes, which have been formed by the action of water in times past. In most areas the soil is very thin and is usually the product of leaf mold.

Development has made inroads on the flora, especially on New Providence, Grand Bahama, and Eleuthera. This appears to be inevitable, as we are in the "age of progress." There does not appear to be any virgin forest anywhere, either pine or mixed broadleaf. However, certain sections of the east coast of Andros and Abaco have some good secondary growth of mixed broadleaf forest, with the canopy varying from 30 to 50 feet. Botanists believe that the virgin forest was 40 to 60 feet in the Bahamas, depending on the area. Today most stands of mixed broadleaf constitute rather a low forest. These areas are very interesting, whether tall or short, as there is quite a variety of trees; more than 100 species to the square mile is not uncommon. In some cases these same species are found growing in a stunted state in areas known locally as the scrublands. Some species are adapted to grow right on the coast, where they are generally quite short, due to the action of the wind and spray.

Pine forest grows on Grand Bahama, Abaco, New Providence, and Andros only. In its virgin state, it grew to about 90 feet tall, but this forest has all been cut. Nevertheless, there are a few good stands of secondary growth, with the best, probably, on South Andros.

The definition of a tree, in this book, is understood to mean a plant with a woody stem that occasionally or often grows, unsupported and erect, to a height of eight to ten feet or more.

The Bahamas have been divided into three sections: North, Central, and South. North is composed of Abaco, Grand Bahama, Bimini, and the Berry Islands. Central is Andros, New Providence, Eleuthera, Exuma, Cat Island, San Salvador, Rum Cay, and Conception Island. South is Long Island, Ragged island, Acklins and Crooked Islands, Long Cay, Mayaguana, and Inagua. The authors do not claim to be completely accurate as to whether a tree is, or is not, excluded from an area. For example, a tree that is listed as growing only in the Central Bahamas could conceivably have spread to a very limited part of the Northern section. Time simply does not permit the exploration of every single area. However, where there are known exceptions they have been noted.

The novice would be well advised to take on no more than six trees to begin with. To mention some very common ones, let us take Gum elemi, Poison wood, Pigeon plum, Lance wood, Crab wood, and Spanish Stopper. When these (or other common ones) are learnt then one can move ahead. It must be pointed out that there is often a good deal of variety within one species, especially in the shape of the leaves, due to environmental conditions. When one becomes more knowledgeable it is entertaining to try identifying by the trunk alone. This is easier said than done, but pays off with some species, as Poison-wood, and is useful in areas where the trees are tall, as it is not always possible to see the foliage clearly.

With regard to common names it is well to remember that these often vary from island to island. In a few cases there are no known common names, and the generic name is used (Zizyphus, Polygala, Neobracea, Rauwolfia, etc.).

THE BAHAMAS NATIONAL TRUST

The heart, the conscience, and the very effective voice for conservation in the Bahamas is the Bahmas is the Bahamas National Trust. A non-profit organization, founded in 1959, it has the support of the Government of the Bahamas, of the international scientific community, and of many conservation-minded lay persons, and enjoys the patronage of His Royal Highness, The Duke of Edinburgh, K. G. It is governed by a Council, two of whose members are appointed by H. E. the Governor General, two by the Minister of Agriculture Fisheries and Local Government, two by the Minister of Tourism, one by the Smithsonian Institute, one by the National Audubon Society, one by the American Museum of Natural History, and nine elected by the general membership at the annual meeting.

In following the recommendations of its scientific advisors, the Trust has secured the acquisition of over 500 square miles of unspoiled wilderness, has undertaken research leading to the protection of endangered species of Bahamian wildlife, and has inaugurated a program of presentation of the conservationist philosophy and data on natural history to the general public and to the schools.

The primary goal of this book is the further stimulation of interest in the vegetation of the Bahamas, in the hope that the resulting understanding and appreciation of the nation's natural treasures will augment the growing conservation movement. In the opinion of the authors, one of the principal and most productive means of sharing in the implementation of these ideals lies in supporting the Trust in its endeavors. Membership information may be obtained by application to the Bahamas National Trust at P. O. Box N-4105, Nassau, N. P., Bahamas.

DEFINITIONS

As this book has been designed for use by the lay person, rather than by the botanist, an attempt has been made to exclude botanical terminology, but a few concepts basic to that science have been employed. Most of these are probably self-explanatory, but a brief discussion of some of them might prove to be of some value.

LEAVES may be simple, with one segment of tissue on each blade (1), or compound (2), with more than one segment (two or many). Of those that are compound, the leaflets may radiate from a central point (palmately compound, 2), or be arranged in two lines with a single leaflet at the end (odd pinnately compound, 4), or end in a pair (even pinnately compound, 5). The leaf may occur singly at the node, the growth center, of the twig (alternate, 6) or with two leaves facing one another (opposite, 7). A few trees carry the leaves bunched at the tips of the twigs to the degree that it is not immediately apparent that they are, in fact, alternate; four such plants are dealt with at the end of the section on alternate leaves (8). The veins within the leaf may radiate from one point (palmate, 9) or may be arranged in rows on the opposite sides of the stem (pinnate, 10); they may give the leaf a netted appearance (reticulate, 11) or they can be hidden in the tissue (obscure, 12).

TWIGS may be smooth, hairy, or marked with scars where the leaves have fallen (13), or with lenticels (14), groups of corky cells that permit the interchange of gases between the tissues and the air.

FLOWERS may grow on stems from the axils (the angle between the leaf and the stem, 15), or at the end of the twigs (terminal, 16), and may be single or in clusters.

The purpose of the key is to assist the reader in identifying the species in question with speed and precision. To that end, the species have been offered in the fashion chosen by grouping those with certain obvious similarities. It must be understood that no two observers could agree completely on the appearance nor on the importance of the characteristics selected, and the compassion of the reader is solicited. Furthermore, the variability within each species of even the major characteristics is so great that a certain number of species will key out to more than one place, and this has caused a certain amount of repetition.

The preliminary key, on the facing page, is designed to divide the host of plant species into smaller categories, based on easily determined characters. Each of these divisions has its own key, appearing on the upper left corner of each left hand page. The key is continuous, running serially throughout the subsequent pages, until the category is exhausted. The common name appears above left, and the scientific name above right, of each species discussed. Where no common name is known, the generic name is employed. The last name in each paragraph is that of the family to which the species had been assigned.

PRELIMINARY KEY

PALMS

1. Leaf pinnate
   2. Fruit 12 inches long; leaflets once-ranked........................ Coconut
   2. Fruit 1 inch long; leaflets several ranked
      3. Fruit red; leaflet stiff; tree short .... Hog Cabbage
      3. Fruit brown; leaflet lax; tree tall .... Royal Palm

COCONUT

HOG CABBAGE PALM

ROYAL PALM

COCONUT PALM
COCOS NUCIFERA

20 - 40 feet, rarely to 100. **TRUNK** solitary, gray-brown, marked with lune-shaped scars of old leafstems, otherwise smooth; usually curving. **CROWN** round, not compact. **LEAFSTEM** heavy, unarmed, not divided at the base, not expanded into a crownshaft. **LEAVES** pinnate, usually about 30; each 15 - 19 feet long, of about 240 leaflets in one row on each side. **FLOWERS** all year; waxy, yellow, 1/3" across, on 3 - 4 foot stalk attached to boat-like spathe; males small, near tip, females large, near base. **FRUIT** all year; nearly round, 1 foot on longest side, green to yellow to brown, the well-known coconut. **FOUND** in coastal areas, all islands. Introduced, possibly as early as 1550, now quite naturalized. The most commonly encountered palm in the Bahamas, and possibly in the tropics of the world; the most obtainable and the easiest to grow. Palmae.

HOG CABBAGE PALM
PSEUDOPHOENIX SARGENTII

10 - 15 feet, rarely to 25. **TRUNK** solitary, erect, ringed, gray, with a prominent crown-shaft. **CROWN** open. **LEAFSTEM** undivided, unarmed, the base expanding into a sheath (crownshaft). **LEAVES** pinnate; usually 10 leaves, each 9 feet long, dark green, of about 90 leaflets arranged in several rows of each side of the leaf. **FLOWERS** all year; yellow, 1/2" across, numerous, on 3 foot stalk. **FRUIT** all year; round, red to red-orange, 3/4" across, sometimes two or three joined together. **FOUND** in Central and Southern Bahamas (Florida keys, Cuba, Hispaniola, Yucatan); widely used, where available, as an ornamental. Palmae.

ROYAL PALM
ROYSTONIA REGIA

80-120 feet. **TRUNK** solitary, massive, gray, smooth, with a prominent crownshaft. **CROWN** fairly compact. **LEAFSTEM** undivided, unarmed, extended into a sheath (crownshaft). **LEAVES** pinnate; usually 12 - 16 leaves, each 20 - 25 feet long, bright green, of about 180 leaflets on each side arranged in several rows. **FLOWERS** all year; yellow-green, very small, numerous on 4 foot stalk. **FRUIT** all year; round to oblong, red to purple. **FOUND** throughout the Caribbean Basin, about 17 different species; be-lieved to be introduced to most of the Bahamas, known in wild state only on Little Inagua. Palmae.

1. Leaf costapalmate or palmate
    2. Leaf costapalmate..Pond Top Palm
    2. Leaf palmate
        3. Trunk multiple, leafstem toothed ....Spanish Top Palm
        3. Trunk solitary, leafstem not toothed
            4. Leafstem base split; fruit white...................................Buffalo Top Palm
            4. Leafstem base not split; fruit black..............................Silver Top Palm

SPANISH TOP PALM, SAW PALMETTO

POND TOP PALM

BUFFALO TOP PALM

SILVER TOP PALM

POND TOP PALM   SABAL PALMETTO

15-25 feet, rarely to 80. **TRUNK** thick; may be gray and smooth, or covered with remnants of old leafstems. **CROWN** compact, rounded. **LEAFSTEMS** to 7 feet, unarmed, the base divided. **LEAVES** costapalmate, the curving midrib extending completely through the leaf; usually about 30 leaves, each 5 - 8 feet across, dull medium green, of about 90 segments, each deeply split at the tip and ending in thin threads. **FLOWERS** generally in the spring; very numerous, small inconspicuous, on long stalks. **FRUIT** in summer; persistent; round, black, 3/4" across, barely edible. **FOUND** throughout the Bahamas as a fairly common ornamental, wild in some areas; the segments are used as weaving material. Southeast coast USA, Cuba. Palmae.

SPANISH TOP PALM   ACOELORRHAPHE WRIGHTII

15 - 25 feet, rarely to 40. **TRUNKS** multiple, each under 3" wide; covered with closely woven palm fiber and remnants of old leafstems. **CROWN** round, open; multiple stems of varying ages combine to give the impression of a thicket. **LEAFSTEMS** to 3 feet long, undivided at the base, armed with sharp teeth. **LEAVES** palmate; usually about 30 leaves, each 3 feet wide, light to dark green above, somewhat silvery below, of about 36 to 54 segments, each split at the extreme tip. **FLOWERS** in spring and summer; numerous, inconspicuous, on 2 1/2 foot stalks. **FRUIT** in summer and fall; round, dull orange to black, 1/2" across. **FOUND** only on Andros, in fresh water or brackish swamps; a desirable ornamental when transplanted. Florida, Cuba, Hispaniola. Palmae.

BUFFALO TOP PALM   THRINAX MORRISII

5 - 12 feet, rarely to 30. **TRUNK** solitary, smooth, 4 - 5" wide, the base often swollen. **CROWN** open, irregular. **LEAFSTEMS** 4 - 6 feet long, divided at the base, unarmed. **LEAVES** palmate; usually about 30, each 4 - 8 feet wide, glossy light green above, dull silvery below, of about 50 segments, each split about 4 inches at the tip. **FLOWERS** all year; inconspicuous, on 3 - 6 foot stalk. **FRUIT** all year; round, white, spongy on the outside, 1/5" across. **FOUND** throughout the Bahamas; a fairly good ornamental, but very slow growing. Florida, Cuba. Palmae.

SILVER TOP PALM   COCCOTHRINAX ARGENTATA

3 - 6 feet, rarely to 20. **TRUNK** solitary, smooth, gray, to 6" wide. **CROWN** open, leaves in all directions. **LEAFSTEMS** 2 1/2 feet long, not divided at the base, unarmed. **LEAVES** palmate; usually about 16 leaves, each 3 feet wide, dark green above, silvery below, of about 40 slender segments, each split 2 - 3 inches at the tip. **FLOWERS** in summer; very small, white, on 2 foot stalk. **FRUIT** in late summer and fall; purple to black, 1/4 - 1/3" across. **FOUND** throughout the Bahamas; a good ornamental, but slow growing. Florida, Cuba, Jamaica, Virgin Islands. Palmae.

12

CEDAR, PINE, CASUARINA

1. Leaves scale-like; fruit round, blue ....Red Cedar
1. Leaves (or apparent leaves) needle shaped
    2. True needles, unjointed; fruit a cone...Yellow Pine
    2. Needle-like stems, jointed; fruit spherical.......................................Casuarina

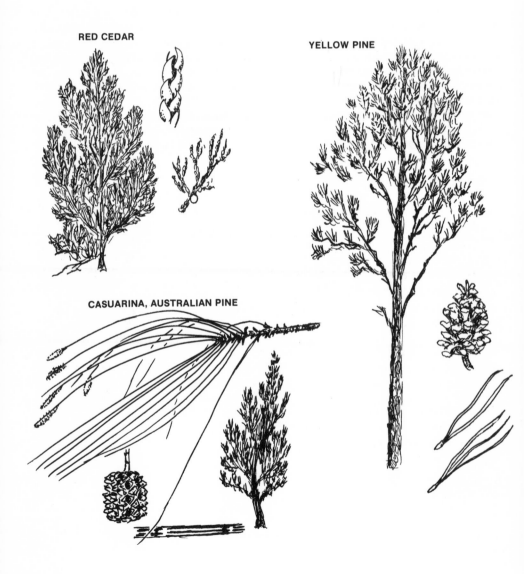

RED CEDAR

YELLOW PINE

CASUARINA, AUSTRALIAN PINE

RED CEDAR
JUNIPERUS BERMUDIANA .

10 - 30 feet. **TRUNK** medium thick, short. **CROWN** spreading or narrow, dense; branches erect, straight. **BARK** brown to red-brown, rough, splitting into small, thin. irregular plates. **TWIGS** green to brown, slender, flexible, curved or straight, rough, scaly; aromatic when broken. **LEAVES** evergreen, very numerous, close, overlapping, almost scale-like (but not sharp); juvenile form narrow, sharp pointed, opposite or in threes, not overlapping; both forms aromatic when crushed. **STROBILI** in late winter or spring; very small, numerous, blue-green, apparently stalkless, axillary; male and female on same or different trees. **FRUIT** in summer; about 1/8" across; more or less round, blue-gray, numerous. **FOUND** in Northern and Central Bahamas, in low areas and along the shore. Cuba, Jamaica. Pinaceae.

YELLOW PINE
PINUS CARIBEA

20 - 50 feet, or taller. **TRUNK** medium to thick, straight. **CROWN** rather narrow, irregular, open; branches erect to horizontal. **BARK** dark gray-brown to brown, very rough, deeply furrowed. broken into irregular plates. **TWIGS** thick, straight, red-brown, growing in spring. **NEEDLES** evergreen, slender, flexible, dark green, sharp-tipped, 6 - 10" long. **STROBILI** in winter; male purple, 1" or more long; female pink-purple, 1/2 - 3/4" long; both about 3/8" thick. **FRUIT** hard woody cone, 3 - 6" long, 1 1/2 - 3" broad, dark brown, persistent. **FOUND** on Grand Bahama, Abaco, New Providence, and Andros. Southeastern USA, Cuba. Pinaceae.

CASUARINA
CASUARINA LITOREA

30 - 70 feet. **TRUNK** thick, straight. **CROWN** narrow, open; branches very long, erect to horizontal, flexible. **TWIGS** green, needle-like, slender, jointed. **LEAVES** at joints of twigs, dark green, about 1/16" long, scale-like. **FLOWERS** in early summer; light red-brown, very numerous, dense, on cylindrical stalks 3/4 - 1 1/2" long and about 1/4" thick; male and female on same tree. **FRUIT** in fall, persistent; gray-green when young, turning brown and hardening; almost round, divided into many segments, about 1" long. **FOUND** throughout the Bahamas; originally introduced, the tree has gone wild and is now accepted as a native; common. Australia and New Guinea, now pan-tropical. Casuarinaceae.

ALTERNATE LEAVES   PALMATE VEINS

1. Leaf margin smooth, leaf not downy
   2. Leaf 5 - 8″ long, dark above ....Mahoe
   2. Leaf 3 - 6″ long, bright green both sides ....Cork Tree

1. Leaf margin lobed, toothed, or irregular
   2. Margin always distinctly lobed, not toothed
      3. Leaf with long central point..Wild Okra
      3. Leaf with short central point ....Wild Hibiscus

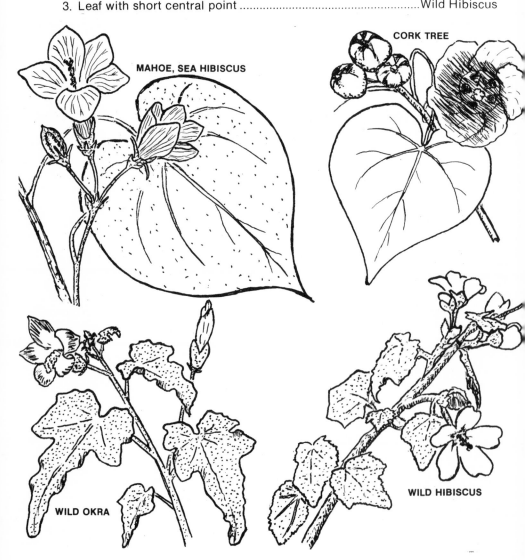

MAHOE, SEA HIBISCUS

CORK TREE

WILD OKRA

WILD HIBISCUS

MAHOE   HIBISCUS TILIACEUS

10 - 20 feet. **TRUNK** rather slender, short, sometimes multiple. **CROWN** very spreading and broad; branches erect to horizontal. **BARK** gray, thin, smooth, strong. **TWIGS** green to brown, thick, straight, smooth, slightly downy. **LEAVES** firm, smooth. yellow-green to dark green and shiny above, paler and downy below; prominently 7-9 nerved, net venation; 4-7" long; stem 2-5" long, tip very short pointed, base heart shape, almost round. **FLOWERS** in summer, occasionally all year; showy, about 4" across, yellow turning red, singly in the axils on long stalks. **FRUIT** in winter, occasionally all year; long pointed, about 3/4" long, brown, opening when dry. **FOUND** in Northern and Central Bahamas, but apparently not on Eleuthera, Cat Island, nor San Salvador; a tree of the coastal areas; not common. Caribbean and Old World tropics, South Florida. Malvaceae.

CORK TREE   THESPESIA POPULNEA

10 - 30 feet. **TRUNK** medium to thick, generally short, rarely multiple. **CROWN** spreading, regular, dense; branches thick, numerous. **BARK** dark brown to dark gray, occasionally almost black with age, very thick and rough in wide furrows. **TWIGS** gray, thick. usually curved, roughened by numerous leaf scars. **LEAVES** clustered at twig ends. smooth, thin, medium firm, dark green and shiny above, paler below; conspicuously 5 nerved; 3 - 5" long and almost as broad; stem stout, 3 - 4" long; tip long pointed, base heart shape. **FLOWERS** in summer, occasionally all year; 2 - 3" long, pale yellow with dark red centre, lasting one day, then pink-purple when dying. **FRUIT** in winter and spring, occasionally all year, persistent; 1 - 1 1/2" across, depressed-globose, dark brown, leathery, splitting. **FOUND** throughout the Bahamas, in low swampy areas; very salt tolerant. Florida, Old World tropics, Caribbean. Malvaceae.

WILD OKRA   HIBISCUS BRITTONIANUS

10 - 15 feet, more often a shrub. **TRUNK** slender, straight. **CROWN** spreading; branches slender, erect or horizontal. **BARK** light gray, thin, with vertical fissures. **TWIGS** green and downy, gray with age, with rounded and raised leaf scars. **LEAVES** medium green. dull, 3 - 5 nerved; 2 - 5" long; stem 3" long or less; margins toothed with broad. soft points; tip blunt, base square cut. **FLOWERS** in spring and summer; single stalked. pale yellow, not fully opening, 3" long, axillary near twig ends. **FRUIT** in late summer or fall; green to brown, a capsule with fine hair, 1" long, 3/4" wide, 4 - 5 compartments. **FOUND** on South Andros and Long Island. Malvaceae.

WILD HIBISCUS   PHYMOSIA ABUTILOIDES

8 - 10 feet, often a shrub. **TRUNK** short. **CROWN** spreading, open; branches erect. **BARK** gray to light brown, thin, strong, slightly rough. **TWIGS** gray to light brown. slender, smooth, somewhat downy. **LEAVES** downy, gray green and dull above, slightly paler below, prominently 5 to 7 nerved; 1 1/2 - 4" long, stem thick, downy, 1" long or more; tip long pointed, base cordate, margin bluntly toothed. **FLOWERS** in winter and spring; showy, pale to medium pink, 5 petals, 1 - 1 1/2" across, stamens 1/2" or less; in short-stalked clusters at twig ends, one or two open at a time. **FRUIT** quickly following the flower; globose, about 1/2" across, brown, becoming dry and splitting into sections. **FOUND** in Northern and Central Bahamas, in cut-over land, not common. Malvaceae.

ALTERNATE LEAVES   PALMATE VEINS

2. Leaf margin toothed or irregular, sometimes lobed
  3. Leaf hairy or downy
    4. Leaf hairy both sides
      5. Leaf dark green above, lighter below .... Soldier Berry
      5. Leaf dark green above, yellow below .... Cow Bush
    4. Leaf not hairy above; sometimes lobed .... Wild Salve
  3. Leaf not hairy nor downy
    4. Twigs hairy; leaf 4 - 6" long .... Swamp Bush

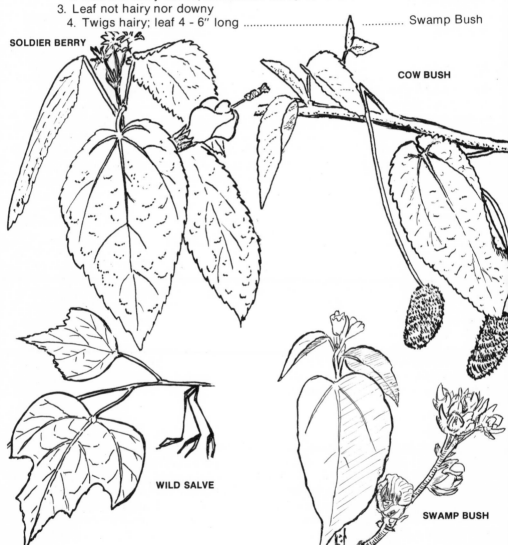

SOLDIER BERRY

COW BUSH

WILD SALVE

SWAMP BUSH

SOLDIER BERRY — MALVAVISCUS ARBOREUS

8 - 15 feet. **TRUNK** slender, flexible, straight. **CROWN** narrow, sparse, or spreading and open; branches slender. drooping. **BARK** gray, smooth, thin, strong. **TWIGS** green to brown, slender, smooth, often hairy. **LEAVES** medium firm, hairy, bright green and dull above, paler and downy below; heavily 5 nerved, sometimes 3 lobed; 2 - 6" long: stem thick, 1 - 2" long; tip long or short pointed, base round or cordate, margins blunt dentate. **FLOWERS** mostly in fall and winter; 1 1/4" across, showy, bright red. not fully opening; on short terminal stalk, singly or in twos and threes. **FRUIT** mostly winter and spring; almost round, 1/3" across, turning brown and dry. **FOUND** on Abaco and Grand Bahama, in mixed broadleaf areas. Cuba. Malvaceae.

COW BUSH — HELICTERES JAMAICENSIS

8 - 15 feet, often a shrub. **TRUNK** short, slender. **CROWN** spreading and very open: branches slender, often drooping. **BARK** light brown, smooth, thin. **TWIGS** light brown. slender, straight, smooth, somewhat downy. **LEAVES** smooth, medium firm. yellow-green and dull above, much paler below, very downy both sides; prominently 5 nerved and net-veined beneath; 2 - 4" long; stem 1/2 - 1" long; tip short or long pointed. base irregularly heart shape, margins bluntly serrate. **FLOWERS** in fall or winter. occasionally all year; singly or in small clusters in axils; about 1" across, white, very showy, with drooping column 2 - 4" long. **FRUIT** in winter or spring, occasionally all year: 1 - 2" long, brown, twisted into a spiral. **FOUND** throughout the Bahamas, in low mixed broadleaf areas and scrubland, in full sunlight. Cuba, Virgin Islands, Jamaica. Sterculiaceae.

WILD SALVE — HELICTERES SEMITRILOBA

10 - 12 feet, often a shrub. **TRUNK** short, slender. **CROWN** spreading, very sparse: branches erect. **BARK** thin, gray, slightly rough. **TWIGS** gray, slender to medium. slightly roughened by horizontal lines and leaf scars. **LEAVES** firm, very dark green. dull, smooth above, much paler, heavily veined and somewhat downy below, 7 nerved: 2 - 4" long, nearly as broad; stem 1" or longer; tip blunt pointed, base nearly heart shape. margins toothed with irregular indentations. **FLOWERS** in fall; 1/3" long. white. becoming reddish; hairy, numerous, in terminal spikes. **FRUIT** in winter and spring: dark brown, straight capsules about 1" long, splitting into five parts. **FOUND** in Central and Southern Bahamas, in scrubland or mixed broadleaf areas of low elevation: not common. Cuba. Hispaniola. Sterculiaceae.

SWAMP BUSH — PAVONIA SPICATA

8 - 15 feet. **TRUNK** slender, short, multiple. **CROWN** very spreading and open: branches numerous, slender. **BARK** gray, smooth, thin, strong. **TWIGS** green to gray. medium to thick, generally curved, smooth, faintly downy. **LEAVES** firm, smooth, thick. bright to dark green and shiny above, much paler below; strongly 5 nerved, net venation: 2 - 5" long; stem thick, faintly downy, 1/2" long or more; tip long pointed, base heart shape. margin smooth or faintly toothed. **FLOWERS** off and on all year; about 1" across. bright green, not fully opening, petals as long as or slightly longer than the stamens: on branched terminal spikes 4" or more long, one or two open at a time. **FRUIT** not seen by authors. **FOUND** on North Andros, though very rare; in dense masses on low ground. Florida, Caribbean Islands and coasts. Malvaceae.

18

ALTERNATE LEAVES   SPINY TWIGS

    4. Twigs not hairy; leaf 1½ - 3″ long.............................Bahama Swamp Bush

1. Leaf ½″ long or less
  2. Leaves borne all along the twig ....Tear Coat
  2. Leaves borne at tip of short, thick twig..Brier Tree

1. Leaf ½″ long or more
  2. Leaf base pointed; leaf shiny, net-veined..Ziziphus

BAHAMA SWAMP BUSH

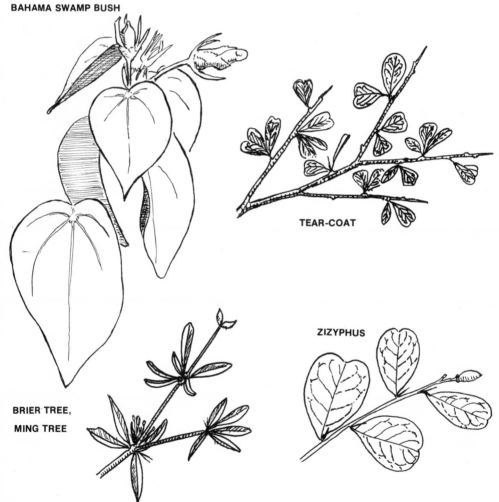

TEAR-COAT

BRIER TREE,
MING TREE

ZIZYPHUS

BAHAMA SWAMP BUSH PAVONIA BAHAMENSIS

8 - 15 feet. **TRUNK** slender to medium, multiple, often forming a dense clump. **CROWN** somewhat spreading; branches erect, numerous. **BARK** dark brown, thin, somewhat rough, often cracking. **TWIGS** green to red-brown, slender to medium, curved, slightly roughened by old leaf scars and lenticels. **LEAVES** smooth, medium firm, bright green and shiny above, slightly paler below; prominently 5-nerved; 2 - 4" long and nearly as broad; stem 1 - 2" long; tip pointed, base heart shape. **FLOWERS** off and on all year: about 1" long, bright green, not fully opening, singly or in twos or threes, at the twig ends on stalks 1" long or more. **FOUND** on San Salvador and Southern Bahamas, in low areas near ponds and salt water sounds; not common. Caicos. Malvaceae.

TEAR COAT SECURINEGA ACIDOTON

8 - 10 feet, or shrubby. **TRUNK** slender, often sprawling. **CROWN** spreading, many long branches. **BARK** pale gray, spongy, with vertical fissures. **TWIGS** gray, slender, zig-zag or crooked; axillary spines 1/2" long. **LEAVES** rigid, often in small clusters; dark green and shiny above, paler below, net venation prominent; 1/4 - 1/2" long; tip broadly blunt or rounded, base wedge, margins smooth. **FLOWERS** small, lacking petals: males clustered, females solitary. **FRUIT** fleshy, then drying; three-angled. **FOUND** in Central Bahamas in scrub and cut-over land. Cuba, Virgin Islands, Jamaica. Euphorbiaceae.

BRIER TREE BUCIDA SPINOSA

10 - 12 feet, or a shrub. **TRUNK** short. **CROWN** very spreading, often flat topped; branches horizontal, zig-zag. **BARK** gray-brown, rough, thick, fissured. **TWIGS** brown, zig-zag, slender, slightly rough, with sharp, branched spines in axils or at ends. **LEAVES** often in whorls; smooth, firm; dark green and shiny above, paler below; net venation: 1/2" long. stem very short; tip rounded or notched, base wedge or narrow. **FLOWERS** summer and fall; 1/8" long, yellow, singly or few in short axil cluster. **FRUIT** in fall or winter; under 1/4" long, ovoid, black. **FOUND** on Grand Bahama, Abaco, and Andros, in low areas, margins of swamps, whitelands. Cuba. Combretaceae.

ZIZIPHUS ZIZIPHUS TAYLORII

10 - 15 feet. **TRUNK** slender, short. **CROWN** irregular, somewhat spreading, dense: branches erect. **BARK** brown, thin, smooth, sometimes cracking into little pieces. **TWIGS** brown, slender, usually curved, roughened by minute furrows; occasionally a short spine or two in an axil. **LEAVES** evergreen, smooth, firm, very dark green and shiny above, faintly shiny below; net venation prominent; 3/4 - 1 1/2" long; stem short, tip rounded or notched, base rounded. **FLOWERS** in summer; less than 1/4" long, greenish yellow, in small, short-stalked clusters, in axils or at end of twig. **FRUIT** in fall: 1/3" long, nearly round, smooth, green turning brown. **FOUND** on most islands, but apparently not on New Providence nor Andros; in rocky scrub-lands. Caicos. Rhamnaceae.

ALTERNATE LEAVES   IRREGULAR MARGINS

  2. Leaf base wedge shaped
    3. Leaf 1/3 - 1/2" long, veins indistinct .... Tallowwood
    3. Leaf 1/2 - 1" long, 2 or more on thick spur .... Spiny Milk Berry
1. Leaf 4" long or more
  2. Teeth sharp, mostly near tip of leaf .... Anaconda
  2. Margin lobed or scalloped
    3. Margin deeply lobed .... Mexican Plume Poppy

TALLOWWOOD,

SPANISH PLUM

SPINY MILK BERRY

MEXICAN PLUME POPPY

ANACONDA,   GEIGER TREE

TALLOWWOOD

XIMENIA AMERICANA

10 - 12 feet, or less. **TRUNK** slender, short, straight or crooked. **CROWN** spreading, irregular; branches erect to horizontal. **BARK** brown to red-brown, thin, smooth, cracking and roughening with age. **TWIGS** green to brown, slender, crooked, smooth or slightly roughened by lenticels; often with straight, sharp spines 1/4" long, singly in axils. **LEAVES** medium firm, smooth, bright yellow-green and shiny above, paler below, venation inconspicuous; 1 - 3 1/2" long; stem 1/4" long; tip blunt, rounded, or notched, base wedge. **FLOWERS** in spring or early summer, or through the year; showy, 1/3" across, four fuzzy yellow petals, fragrant, in small, short-stalked clusters in the axils. **FRUIT** in summer and fall, or through the year; 1/2" long, nearly globose, smooth, yellow, a single hard seed. **FOUND** in Southern Bahamas, but apparently not on Mayaguana and Inagua; along coast or in mixed broadleaf acreas (when near shore, leaves are more fleshy). Florida through South America, also Old World tropics. Olacaceae.

SPINY MILK BERRY

BUMELIA CELASTRINA

8 - 15 feet, or shrubby. **TRUNK** slender, short. **CROWN** irregular; branches slender, erect. **BARK** brown to dark gray, thin, rough, furrowed. **TWIGS** gray to brown, slender, smooth, with sharp ridged spines 1/4" long in the axils, single or paired. **LEAVES** often in clusters; firm, smooth, dark green and dull above and below; venation obscure; 1/2 - 1" long; stem very short; tip rounded, base narrow or wedge. **FLOWERS** in fall and winter; 1/8" long, yellow-green, fragrant, numerous, in short-stalked axillary clusters. **FRUIT** in early summer; 1/3" long, oval, purple-black, smooth, dull, edible but gummy. **FOUND** in Central Bahamas, inland, in low areas and around ponds. Florida, Cuba. Sapotaceae.

ANACONDA

CORDIA SEBESTENA

10 - 20 feet. **TRUNK** slender to medium, short, sometimes crooked. **CROWN** somewhat spreading, sometimes narrow, dense; branches erect, stiff. **BARK** dark brown, thick, very rough, in irregular vertical furrows. **TWIGS** gray, thick, straight, smooth, with a few lenticels. **LEAVES** dark green and rough above, paler and smoother below; pinnate venation prominent; 3 - 6" long; stem thick, 1 - 2" long; tip short pointed or rounded, base round or heart shape, margins slightly toothed. **FLOWERS** off and on all year, mainly in summer; about 1 1/2" across, scarlet, very showy, in dense clusters at or near the twig end of stalks about 1 foot long. **FRUIT** off and on all year, mainly in summer and fall; about 1 1/22" long, white, smooth, with a small crown at the tip. **FOUND** throughout the Bahamas, mainly in coastal areas; common on some of the smaller cays. Florida, Caribbean. Boraginaceae.

PLUME POPPY

BOCCONIA FRUTESCENS

8 - 10 feet, more often a shrub. **TRUNK** short, slender, **CROWN** spreading, sparse, of several erect, usually curved branches with prominent twig scars. **BARK** thin, gray, rough; orange-brown inside. **TWIGS** gray-brown, very thick, smooth with large leaf scars. **LEAVES** pennatifid, clustered at twig ends, smooth, yellow-green and dull above, gray green and paler below; midrib thick, hairy; 5 - 10" long; stem thick, 1" long or more. **FLOWERS** in winter; numerous, 1/8" long, on much branched spike 8" long or more. **FRUIT** in summer; numerous, 1/8" long, light brown, one shiny black seed in red flesh. **FOUND** on Abaco in two places — probably recent introduction (birds). Cuba Papaveraceae.

ALTERNATE LEAVES   IRREGULAR MARGINS

   3. Margin scalloped..Cahoney

1. Leaf less than 4" long
  2. Leaf margin spiny
    3. Leaf less than 2" long
      4. Leaf white below..Candlewood
      4. Leaf pale green below
        5. Venation prominent..False Holly
        5. Venation not prominent ....Wild Holly

CAHONEY, WILD AVOCADO

CANDLEWOOD

FALSE HOLLY

WILD HOLLY

CAHONEY
CASEARIA GUIDONIA

15 - 30 feet. **TRUNK** slender to medium, tall, straight, sometimes with irregular swellings. **CROWN** spreading, medium dense to rather open; branches straight, erect, becoming horizontal with age. **BARK** brown, slender, slightly zig-zag, smooth with occasional lenticels. **LEAVES** smooth, firm, dark green, shiny, faintly downy above, paler and downy below; midrib prominent, venation net; 3 - 6" long and 2 - 5" broad; stem 1/2" long or less; tip long or short pointed, base wedge or rounded. **FLOWERS** in spring and early summer; small, cream-coloured, numerous, on axillary stalks; very fragrant. **FRUIT** in spring and early summer; about 2" across, globose, dark green or tinged red-brown, smooth, shiny, not edible. **FOUND** in northern and Central Bahamas, but apparently not on San Salvador; reasonably common in mixed broadleaf areas. Cuba, Jamaica. Flacourtiaceae.

CANDLEWOOD.
GOCHNATIA ILICIFOLIA

10 - 15 feet, often a shrub. **TRUNK** slender, short, straight. **CROWN** narrow, medium dense; branches erect. **BARK** dark gray to brown, thin, rough in furrows. **TWIGS** light gray to almost white, slender, smooth or slightly roughened by horizontal lines. **LEAVES** evergreen, firm, smooth, dark green and shiny above, very white beneath; prominent midrib, net venation; about 1" long; stem short; tip blunt or rounded, base wedge or narrow, margins with a few spiny teeth. **FLOWERS** in spring and early summer; about 1" long, showy, erect, orange, resembling a shaving brush; on short terminal stalk, singly or in few-flowered clusters. **FRUIT** in summer; about 1/2" long, yellow-brown. **FOUND** on Abaco, Andros, New Providence, Cat Island. Cuba. Compositae.

FALSE HOLLY
DRYPETES MUCRONATA

8 - 12 feet, often a shrub. **CROWN** spreading, medium dense; branches numerous, horizontal, often mottled gray-brown. **BARK** gray, often mottled gray-brown, thin, smooth. **TWIGS** light to dark gray, slender, zig-zag, roughened by leaf scars and numerous lenticels. **LEAVES** evergreen, very stiff, smooth, dark green and shiny above, paler below; prominent net venation; 1 - 2" long; stem very short; tip very sharp pointed, base unequal or rounded; margins of some leaves with 1 - 4 spiny teeth. **FLOWERS** in early and midsummer; male and female on different trees; males in small short-stalked clusters, females single or few in leaf axils. **FRUIT** in fall and winter; about 1/3" across, round, velvety, more or less white. **FOUND** on Andros and Grand Bahama, in mixed broadleaf areas; not common. Cuba. Euphorbiaceae.

WILD HOLLY
XYLOSMA BUXIFOLIUM

10 - 20 feet. **TRUNK** slender, straight, short, generally armed with numerous slender branched spines. **BARK** brown to gray, sometimes blotched with black, smooth, thin, cracking into pieces when older. **TWIGS** gray to light brown, slender, straight or crooked, smooth except for old leaf scars and lenticels. **LEAVES** very firm and smooth, dark green and very shiny above, paler below; venation not prominent; 1/4 - 1" long; stem about 1/8" long; tip sharp pointed or rounded, often toothed; base narrow wedge; one to four short spiny teeth on margin. **FLOWERS** in fall and winter; male and female on different trees; both yellow-green, less than 1/8" across, female slightly larger than male; in very short-stalked groups of 2 or 3 in leaf axils. **FRUIT** in winter and spring; 1/4" long or less, ovoid to globose, red, smooth, drying black. **FOUND** in Northern and Central Bahamas, but not on San Salvador; a small tree of mixed broadleaf areas and a shrub of pinelands. Flacourtiaceae.

ALTERNATE LEAVES   IRREGULAR MARGINS

   3. Leaf usually over 2″ long
     4. Few (less than 10) spines ....Dahoon Holly
     4. Many (over 20) spines...Young Manchioneel
  2. Leaf margin toothed, scalloped, or irregular; not spiny
   3. Leaf surface shiny
     4. Leaf with soft pointed teeth
       5. Teeth fewer than 8.. Bay Berry
       5. Teeth more than 10
         6. Tip long, twig thin, stem under 1/2″...........................Smooth Casearia

DAHOON HOLLY

YOUNG MANCHIONEEL,

GRIMM'S TREE

BAY BERRY, WILD TEA

SMOOTH CASEARIA

DAHOON

8 - 15 feet. **TRUNK** slender, straight. **CROWN** generally regular, dense, narrow, sometimes sparse and irregular; branches erect. **BARK** gray, downy, thick; darker on older trees. **TWIGS** green to gray, slender, smooth, with occasional lenticels. **LEAVES** evergreen, firm, smooth, bright to dark green and shiny above, paler below; prominent midrib, net venation; 2 - 4" long; stem about 1/3" long; tip short pointed, notched, or rounded; base wedge; margins with a few short teeth from midpoint to tip. **FLOWERS** in spring and early summer; male and female on different trees; numerous, less than 1/4" across, white, in short-stalked clusters in the axils. **FRUIT** in summer and fall; 1/4" across or less, globose, bright red, showy, numerous. **FOUND** on Grand Bahama and Abaco, in or near marshy areas; rather rare. S.E. USA, Cuba. Aquifoliaceae.

YOUNG MANCHIONEEL   GRIMMEODENDRON EGLANDULOSUM

10 - 15 feet, more often a shrub. **TRUNK** short, straight. **CROWN** spreading, regular, open; branches straight, horizontal to erect. **BARK** brown, thin, smooth. **TWIGS** brown, straight, thick, conspicuously ringed by old leaf scars; exuding milky, poisonous sap when broken. **LEAVES** smooth, firm, very dark green and shiny above, paler below; midrib prominent, venation obscure; 1 1/2 - 3" long; stem 1" long or less; tip pointed, base narrow, margins toothed from tip to base. **FLOWERS** in spring and early summer; male and female very small, yellow-green, on same 1 - 2" long spike at twig end. **FRUIT** in summer and fall; trilobed, about 1/3" across, more or less round, green turning brown-blotched; poisonous if eaten. **FOUND** in Central Bahamas, but not on Eleuthera nor Cat Island; common in some areas, as Andros. Cuba. Must be handled with care, as the sap is an irritant (skin blisters). Euphorbiaceae.

BAY BERRY   MYRICA CERIFERA

10 - 20 feet. **TRUNK** slender to medium, short. **CROWN** generally rather spreading, dense; branches slender, horizontal. **BARK** light gray, often mottled, smooth, thin. **TWIGS** gray to brown, smooth, straight, slender. **LEAVES** evergreen, smooth, medium firm, bright to dark green and shiny above, lighter below; venation not prominent; 1 1/2 - 4" long; stem about 1/4" long; tip short to long pointed, base tapered or wedge, margins conspicuously blunt toothed, occasionally smooth; aromatic when crushed. **FLOWERS** in spring and early summer; male and female on different trees, both very small, axillary, male on spikes about 1" long, yellow-green; female on spikes about 1/2" long, light green. **FRUIT** in fall and winter; numerous, round, about 1/8" across, very short-stalked, green-blue. **FOUND** throughout the Bahamas, usually in low areas, wet ground, occasionally in pineland and mixed broadleaf areas. Atlantic and Gulf Coasts, USA, Cuba to Puerto Rico. Myricaceae.

SMOOTH CASEARIA   CASEARIA NITIDA

10 - 15 feet. **TRUNK** slender, straight. **CROWN** rather narrow, generally regular, medium dense; branches slender, horizontal to erect. **BARK** gray-brown, thin, smooth. **TWIGS** brown, slender, zig-zag or crooked, smooth. **LEAVES** smooth, firm, dark green and shiny above, slightly paler below; midrib and pinnate venation fairly prominent; 1 - 2 1/2" long; stem about 1/2" long; tip long pointed, base round or unequal, margins slightly serrate, sometimes wavy; leaf turning brown-purple with age. **FLOWERS** in spring and early summer; about 1/4" across, creamy, single to few, on axillary spikes about 1" long. **FRUIT** in summer; 1/3" across or less; round, shiny, smooth. **FOUND** in Central Bahamas; not a common tree; in mixed broadleaf areas. Cuba. Flacourtiaceae. NOTE: Whitewood (Drypetes diversifolia) and False Holly (D. mucronata) may have some leaves with a few spiny teeth on the margins.

ALTERNATE LEAVES   IRREGULAR MARGINS

      6. Tip short, twig thick, stem 1/2″ .... Manchioneel
   4. Leaf margin scalloped
     5. Upper surface rough ....Crabwood
     5. Upper surface smooth
      6. Twigs green at tip.. Olive Wood
      6. Twigs red-brown at tip..Cuban Holly

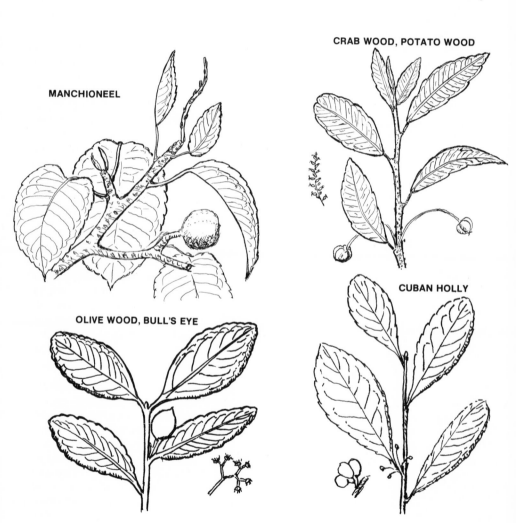

MANCHIONEEL

CRAB WOOD, POTATO WOOD

OLIVE WOOD, BULL'S EYE

CUBAN HOLLY

MANCHIONEEL — HIPPOMANE MANCINELLA

10 - 25 feet. **TRUNK** medium to thick, rather short, often leaning. **CROWN** spreading, medium dense, often regular; branches erect. **BARK** gray-brown, blotched, smooth, thin, becoming somewhat rough on older trees. **TWIGS** gray-brown, thick, curved, roughened by numerous leaf scars; milky sap poisonous. **LEAVES** firm, smooth, dark green and very shiny above, paler below; very prominent midrib, net venation; 1 1/2 - 3 1/2" long; stem 1 - 1 1/2" long; tip blunt pointed or rounded, base rounded, margins faintly serrate. **FLOWERS** in spring, sometimes summer and fall; male and female on same spike; males numerous, very small; females few at base of terminal spike 3 - 6" long. **FRUIT** in summer, sometimes fall and winter; about 1" across, light yellow-green, rounded; very poisonous if eaten. **FOUND** throughout the Bahamas in mixed broadleaf areas usually at or near the coast; fortunately, nowhere common. The sap can cause intense skin irritation and eating the fruit can cause death. Florida, West Indies, tropical continental America. Euphorbiaceae.

CRAB WOOD — ATERAMNUS LUCIDUS

10 - 25 feet. **TRUNK** slender, straight. **CROWN** narrow, sparse to medium dense; branches erect. **BARK** gray to brown, often mottled, smooth, thin, sometimes flaking into small pieces. **TWIGS** brown, slender, straight, slightly roughened by many lenticels and leaf scars. **LEAVES** evergreen, firm, dark green and shiny above, paler below; prominent reticulate venation, especially on upper surface; 1 - 4" long, 3/4 - 1 1/2" broad; stem about 1/4" long; tip blunt pointed or somewhat rounded, base wedge or narrow, margins smooth or faintly serrate. **FLOWERS** in spring, sometimes in fall; male and female on same tree; male very small, yellow-green, numerous, on spikes 1 - 2" long; female single, on longer stalk; both axillary, fragrant. **FRUIT** in summer, sometimes early winter; green turning dark brown, about 1/3" across, nearly round, 3 lobed, on pendant stalk 1 1/2" long or more. **FOUND** throughout the Bahamas, very common; wood very hard. Florida and West Indies. Euphorbiaceae.

OLIVE WOOD — CASSINE XYLOCARPA

10 - 25 feet. **TRUNK** medium to thick, short. **CROWN** spreading, medium dense; branches medium, erect. **BARK** gray-brown, generally blotched, smooth, thick. **TWIGS** green to brown, thick, straight, slightly rough. **LEAVES** evergreen, alternate or opposite, smooth, firm, yellow-green to dark green and shiny above, paler below; fine net venation; 1 - 3" long; stem thick, 1/4" long or less; tip rounded or blunt, base wedge, margins strongly recurved. **FLOWERS** in winter, or off and on all year; less than 1/4" across, green, single or several in the axils on very short stalks. **FRUIT** in summer, or all year; globose, about 1/2" across, yellow; a single hard seed. **FOUND** on Abaco, San Salvador, Crooked and Fortune Islands, and Inagua; in coastal and mixed broadleaf areas. Cuba. Celastraceae.

CUBAN HOLLY — ILEX REPANDA

15 - 30 feet. **TRUNK** medium, straight. **CROWN** usually irregular and somewhat spreading; branches erect. **BARK** light gray, smooth, thin, sometimes mottled with age. **TWIGS** gray, slender, crooked, smooth, often red-brown at the ends. **LEAVES** smooth, stiff, yellow-green to dark green and shiny above, dull yellow-green below; venation pinnate; 1 - 3" long; stem about 1/4" long; tip short pointed or blunt, base wedge; margins often recurved, sometimes faintly serrate. **FLOWERS** in spring; male and female on different trees; both small, pale green, very short-stalked, numerous, in leaf axils. **FRUIT** in summer; about 1/4" across, round, bright red, showy, numerous. **FOUND** in Northern and Central Bahamas, but not on Cat Island, Exuma, nor San Salvador; mainly in mixed broadleaf areas, sometimes in pine forests. Often not recognized as a holly, as the leaves are not conspicuously toothed. Cuba. Aquifoliaceae.

ALTERNATE LEAVES   IRREGULAR MARGINS

3. Leaf surface dull
  4 Margin regularly toothed
    5 Leaf dark green .... Trema
    5. Leaf gray-green .... Velvet Bush
  4. Margin irregular .... Wild Oak

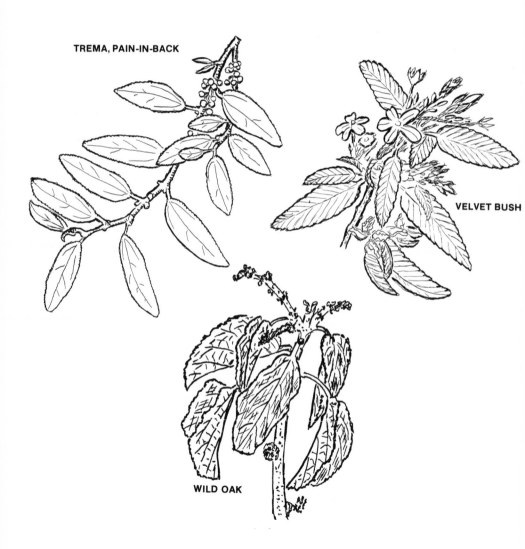

TREMA, PAIN-IN-BACK

VELVET BUSH

WILD OAK

TREMA   TREMA LAMARCKIANA

10 - 12 feet, often a shrub. **TRUNK** slender, short. **CROWN** spreading, rather open; branches slender, erect, long. **BARK** brown, smooth, thin, strong. **TWIGS** green to brown, slender, straight or a bit curved, smooth, downy. **LEAVES** downy and rather soft, dark green and dull above, much paler below; three prominent main veins; 1 - 2 1/2" long; stem 1/2" long or less; tip long or short pointed, base rounded, margins serrate. **FLOWERS** off and on all year; in dense short-stalked axillary clusters, very small and numerous. **FRUIT** off and on all year; round, pink, numerous, less than 1/8" across. **FOUND** throughout the Bahamas, generally in cut-over land, occasionally in scrublands or edges of pine forests; a rapid grower, intolerant of shade. Florida, Bermuda, Cuba, Puerto Rico. Ulmaceae.

VELVET BUSH   MELOCHIA TOMENTOSA

8 - 10 feet, often a shrub. **TRUNK** slender, short. **CROWN** narrow, sparse; branches slender, erect. **BARK** dark red-brown, thin, more or less smooth. **TWIGS** red-brown, very slender, straight, smooth but for leaf scars. **LEAVES** medium firm, smooth, gray-green and dull above, paler below, downy on both sides; prominent pinnate venation; 1 - 1 1/2" long; stem 1/2" long or less; tip blunt pointed, base rounded, margins blunt serrate. **FLOWERS** off and on all year; about 1/3" across, quite showy, pink to dark pink with yellow centre; in few-flowered terminal or axillary clusters. **FRUIT** off and on all year; about 1/4" long, light brown, more or less round. **FOUND** throughout the Bahamas, primarily in cut-over land or scrubland, where it may be common. West Indies, Texas, Mexico. Sterculiaceae.

WILD OAK   LASIOCROTON BAHAMENSIS

8 - 15 feet, often a shrub. **TRUNK** slender. **CROWN** spreading, very open and sparse; branches erect. **BARK** light gray, often blotched, smooth, becoming somewhat rough with age. **TWIGS** light gray, straight or a bit curved, roughened by lenticels. **LEAVES** usually at the twig ends; firm, rough, dull yellow-green above, somewhat hairy and near-white below; pinnate venation very prominent, especially below; veins golden-brown; 2 - 3 1/2" long; stem 1" long or more; tip short pointed, base wedge or rounded. **FLOWERS** off and on all year; male and female on same tree; male very small and numerous, female single or few in short axillary and terminal spikes. **FRUIT** all year; dark green, dull, three angled, slightly hiary capsule about 1/3" across. **FOUND** on South Andros and South Exuma, though not common, in mixed broadleaf areas and scrublands. Cuba, Jamaica. Euphorbiaceae.

ALTERNATE LEAVES   HAIRY SURFACE

1. Rusty hair on under surface only
   2. Leaf dark green above, many fine veins ....Saffron
   2. Leaf light green, few large veins...................................Common Snake Bark
1. White hair on both surfaces
   2. Leaf over 4" long, very flexible ....Salve Bush
   2. Leaf under 4" long, medium firm......................................Cuban Snake Bark

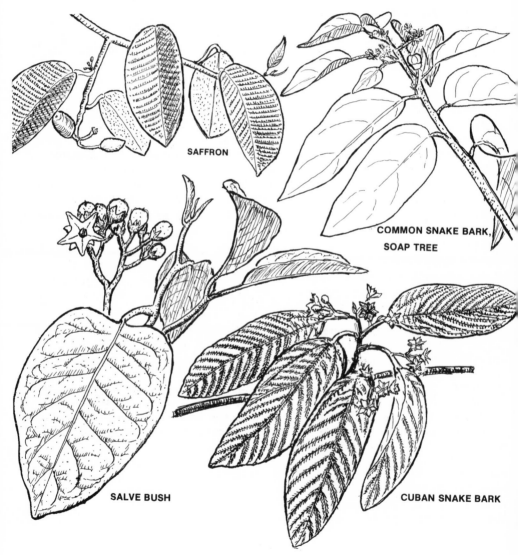

SAFFRON

COMMON SNAKE BARK,
SOAP TREE

SALVE BUSH

CUBAN SNAKE BARK

SAFFRON
CHRYSOPHYLLUM OLIVIFORME

10 - 30 feet. **TRUNK** slender to medium, straight. **CROWN** narrow, medium dense; branches short, erect. **BARK** gray-brown, thick, rough in furrows. **TWIGS** rust-brown to brown, slender, straight or curved, smooth, downy, numerous lenticels. **LEAVES** smooth, firm, very dark green and shiny above, golden brown and downy below; midrib prominent, venation pinnate; 1 - 4" long; stem about 1/2" long; tip short pointed or rounded, base round. **FLOWERS** in fall or early winter; about 1/8" long, light green, slightly fragrant, numerous in short-stalked axillary clusters. **FRUIT** in late winter and spring; about 1/2" long, purple-black, oval or nearly round, smooth, shiny, sweet, edible but slightly gummy. **FOUND** on Abaco, Andros, New Providence, Eleuthera; in mixed broadleaf areas as a tree, in pinelands as a shrub; fairly common. Florida, Jamica to Puerto Rico. Sapotaceae.

COMMON SNAKE BARK
COLUBRINA ARBORESCENS

10 - 25 feet. **TRUNK** slender to medium, straight. **CROWN** somewhat spreading, regular medium dense; branches erect to horizontal. **BARK** gray, smooth, thin. **TWIGS** slender, straight, smooth, with fine rust-brown down near the tip. **LEAVES** smooth, medium firm, dark green and shiny above, paler below; prominent midrib, pinnate venation; 2 - 4" long stem; stem 1" long or more; tip long-pointed, base rounded; underside often heavily covered with fine rust-brown down. **FLOWERS** in late summer and fall; very small, green above and brown below, in small clusters on axillary stalks about 1/2" long, covered with rust-brown down. **FRUIT** in winter; about 1/4" across, brown, more or less round, opening to small shiny black seeds. **FOUND** throughout the Bahamas: reasonably common in some mixed broadleaf areas. Florida, Jamaica. Cuba through Virgin Islands. Rhamnaceae.

SALVE BUSH
SOLANUM ERIANTHUM.

8 - 15 feet, sometimes a shrub. **TRUNK** slender to medium, short. **CROWN** very spreading, open; branches erect, numerous. **BARK** gray, thin, smooth, sometimes warty, slightly furrowed with age. **TWIGS** green to gray, thick, straight or slightly curved, smooth, very downy. **LEAVES** smooth, very downy both sides, dull green above, gray beneath; prominent pinnate venation, thick midrib; 4 - 7" long; stem thick, 1" long or more; tip long or short pointed, base wedge. **FLOWERS** off and on all year; about 1/2" across, white with yellow centre, in small clusters on thick branched stalks 4" long or more. **FRUIT** off and on all year; about 3/4" across, globose, yellow-green, somewhat downy. **FOUND** throughout the Bahamas, very common in open areas. Florida, West Indies, Mexico, Old World. Solanaceae.

CUBAN SNAKE BARK
COLUBRINA CUBENSIS

8 - 10 feet, often a shrub. **TRUNK** slender. **CROWN** somewhat spreading, sparse; branches erect. **BARK** brown, thin, smooth. **TWIGS** green to brown, slender, straight, smooth, somewhat downy. **LEAVES** medium firm, yellow-green to dark green, shiny and slightly crinkled above, much paler and faintly downy below; very prominent pinnate venation; 1 - 3 1/2" long; stem 1/2" long or less; tip blunt pointed, base wedge or unequal. **FLOWERS** in summer; less than 1/4" across, light green. **FRUIT** in fall and early winter; about 1/3" across, globose, brown, smooth. **FOUND** on North Eleuthera only, in mixed broadleaf areas. Florida, Cuba, Hispaniola. Rhamnaceae.

ALTERNATE LEAVES　　　　　　WIDE TIP

1. Leaf (including stem) generally less than 3" long
   2. Leaf smooth, veins not prominent, not scaly
      3. Leaf firm, flat, aromatic when crushed.................................. Cinnamon Bark
      3. Leaf curled, not aromatic..Myrsine
   2. Leaf with prominent veins or scales below
      3. Leaf with prominent veins...Caper Tree
      3. Leaf with scales below ....Wild Orange

CINNAMON BARK

MYRSINE

CAPER TREE

WILD ORANGE, JAMAICA CAPER

CINNAMON BARK
CANELLA WINTERANA

10 - 20 feet. **TRUNK** slender to medium, straight. **CROWN** narrow, dense, but spreading on older trees; branches erect. **BARK** gray to brown, thin, smooth, furrowed with age; very strong scent when cut. **TWIGS** green to brown, straight or slightly curved, somewhat roughened by horizontal lines and leaf scars; strong scent when broken. **LEAVES** evergreen, smooth, very firm, dark green and shiny above, dull and paler below; net venation; 2 - 4" long; stem about 1/4" long, tip blunt pointed, base wedge or unequal; about 1/3" across, showy, red-purple, in short-stalked clusters at twig ends. **FRUIT** in winter and spring; about 1/2" across, globose, dark red, slightly downy, with several shiny black seeds. **FOUND** throughout the Bahamas; rather common in mixed broadleaf areas. Florida, West Indies. Canellaceae.

MYRSINE
MYRSINE FLORIDANA

10 - 25 feet. **TRUNK** slender to medium, straight. **CROWN** narrow, regular, medium dense; branches erect. **BARK** gray, thin, smooth, sometimes fissured on older trees. **TWIGS** green to gray-brown, slender to medium, erect, smooth but for numerous leaf scars. **LEAVES** firm, smooth, dark green and somewhat shiny above, paler below; midrib prominent, venation inconspicuous; 1 1/2 - 4" long; stem thick, about 1/4" long; tip blunt pointed, rounded, or notched; base wedge, margins slightly recurved. **FLOWERS** in winter and spring; about 1/8" across, cream turning red-brown, numerous, almost stalkless, along the length of the twig. **FRUIT** in late winter, spring, and early summer; 1/4" across or less, round, black, smooth. **FOUND** throughout the Bahamas, but apparently not on Inagua; common in pinelands, scrub, or mixed broadleaf areas. Florida. Caribbean Islands, South America. Myrsinaceae.

CAPER
CAPPARIS FLEXUOSA

10 - 20 feet, often a vine-like shrub. **TRUNK** slender, often sprawling or vine-like. **CROWN** irregular, medium dense or rather open; branches erect or drooping and vine-like. **BARK** brown, thin, smooth; sometimes slightly rough with age. **TWIGS** brown, slender, zig-zag, smooth but for tiny lenticels. **LEAVES** firm, smooth with raised veins, yellow-green to light green and somewhat shiny above, paler below; net venation prominent; 1 1/2 - 4" long; stem 1/4" long or less; tip sharp pointed, rounded, or notched; base sharply wedge or rounded; margins revolute. **FLOWERS** in spring or summer; 2 - 4 at twig ends, short stalked, about 2" across, petals white to rose, filaments to 2" long, white, numerous. **FRUIT** in late summer and fall; 3 - 8" long, slender, cylindrical, resembling a bean pod; the seeds imbedded in scarlet pulp. **FOUND** on Andros, Exuma, and Long Island, in mixed broadleaf areas; not common. Florida, Cuba to Barbadoes, Central and South America. Capparidaceae.

WILD ORANGE
CAPPARIS CYNOPHALLOPHORA

10 - 25 feet. **TRUNK** slender to medium, straight. **CROWN** rounded or spreading, dense; branches numerous, many twigs. **BARK** brown, thin, smooth on young trees; rough, breaking into small rounded flakes with age. **TWIGS** brown or gray, scurfy, slender, straight, with occasional leaf scars; often with two or more deeply indented lines running down the twig; sometimes swollen for an inch or so below the point of attachment to the leaf. **LEAVES** smooth, firm, yellow-green to dark green and shiny above, prominently rusty-scaly or silvery below; midvein prominent; 1 1/2 - 4" long; stem about 1" long; tip pointed or notched, base rounded or broad wedge, margins revolute; young leaves narrow, linear. **FLOWERS** in spring and early summer; petals white, 3/4" across, filaments (stamens) over 2" long, purple, with yellow anthers; in clusters of 3 - 10 at twig ends. **FRUIT** in summer and fall; slender cylindrical pod 4 - 16" long, gray-green, scurfy, on long thin stem; seeds brown in red pulp. **FOUND** in Southern Bahamas and San Salvador, in mixed broadleaf areas. Florida, Cuba to Barbadoes. Capparidaceae.

ALTERNATE LEAVES   WIDE TIP

1. Leaf (including stem) generally less than 3" long
  2. Veins prominent
    3. Leaf less than 1" long .... Rat Wood
    3. Leaf more than 1" long
      4. Leaf base wedge shape
        5. Underside rusty...Milk Berry
        5. Underside pale green
          6. Leaf light green, tip a sharp point .... Box Wood
          6. Leaf dark green, tip rounded................................. Bahama Maidenbush

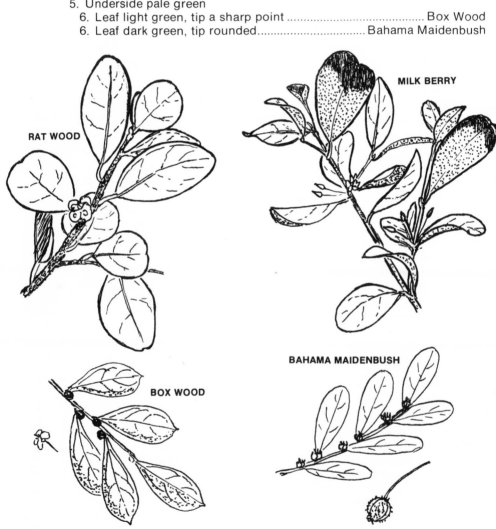

RAT WOOD

MILK BERRY

BOX WOOD

BAHAMA MAIDENBUSH

RAT WOOD   ERYTHROXYLUM ROTUNDIFOLIUM

15 - 35 feet. **TRUNK** slender to medium, straight or crooked. **CROWN** spreading, medium dense; branches slender to medium, erect. **BARK** brown to red-brown, thin, smooth. **TWIGS** brown to red-brown, sometimes blotched, slender, straight or a little curved, slightly roughened by numerous lenticels and sometimes by faint lines. **LEAVES** firm, smooth, bright to dark green and shiny above, gray-green below; 1/3 - 1/2" long; stem about 1/8" long, tip rounded or notched, base narrow. **FLOWERS** in spring and early summer; 1/8" long or less, pale green, single or few in axils, very short stalked, fragrant. **FRUIT** in late summer or fall; bright red, smooth, about 1/8" long, oblong. **FOUND** throughout the Bahamas, in mixed broadleaf areas; common. Cuba, Puerto Rico, Jamaica. Erythroxylaceae.

MILK BERRY   BUMELIA AMERICANA

10 - 20 feet. **TRUNK** medium to thick, short. **CROWN** spreading, rounded, dense; branches horizontal. **BARK** gray-brown, smooth when young, rough furrows with age. **TWIGS** gray, often mottled, straight or a bit curved, smooth but for numerous leaf scars. **LEAVES** smooth, firm, dark green and shiny above, slightly paler or more often rusty brown below; venation pinnate; 3/4 - 2" long; stem 1/4" long or less; tip rounded or notched, base narrow or wedge, margins often recurved. **FLOWERS** off and on all year, mainly winter and spring; small, pale green, numerous, fragrant, on short axillary stalks. **FRUIT** off and on all year, mainly in summer; about 1/3" long, almost round, black, smooth, shiny; edible though slightly gummy. **FOUND** throughout the Bahamas, generally in coastal areas, sometimes inland in mixed broadleaf areas; fairly common. The alternate leaves may appear to be opposite. Sapotaceae.

BOX WOOD   SCHAEFFERIA FRUTESCENS

10 - 20 feet. **TRUNK** slender, short. **CROWN** regular, medium dense; branches slender, erect, numerous. **BARK** light brown, thin, smooth on young trees, thick and rough in shallow fissures with age. **TWIGS** green to gray, slender, smooth, with occasional leaf scars **LEAVES** smooth, firm, bright green and shiny above, somewhat paler below prominent net venation; 1 1/2 - 2 1/2" long; stem about 1/4" long; tip short pointed or rounded, base wedge. **FLOWERS** in spring and summer; male and female on different trees; both very small, in short-stalked axillary clusters. **FRUIT** in fall and winter, occasionally persisting through spging; less than 1/4" across, more or less round, red to yellow. **FOUND** throughout the Bahamas, in mixed broadleaf areas. Florida. Jamaica Cuba to Grenada. Celastraceae.

BAHAMA MAIDENBUSH   SAVIA BAHAMENSIS

10 - 20 feet. **TRUNK** slender, straight. **CROWN** rather narrow, dense; branches erect, numerous. **BARK** gray to brown, often blotched, smooth, thin, roughening and cracking with age. **TWIGS** gray to brown, slender, straight, roughened by numerous lenticels. **LEAVES** evergreen, smooth, firm, dark green and shiny above, paler below; venation reticulate; 3/4 - 2 1/2" long; stem about 1/8" long; tip rounded or blunt pointed, base wedge or rounded. **FLOWERS** in spring, sometimes in fall; male and female on different trees; males very small, in short-stalked axillary clusters; females single or few, on short stalks. **FRUIT** in summer, occasionally in fall; green turning brown and drying; 1/4 - 1/3" across, round, three lobed. **FOUND** throughout the Bahamas, common in most mixed broadleaf areas. Florida, Jamaica, Cuba. Euphorbiaceae.

ALTERNATE LEAVES   WIDE TIP

    4. Leaf base rounded
      5. Leaf 1 1/2" - 3" long...Cocoplum
      5. Leaf 3/4 - 1" long...Polygala
  2. Veins indistinct
   3. Leaf tip pointed
     4. Leaf stiff, with short sharp tip .... Milk Tree
     4. Leaf not stiff; tip blunt or rounded
      5. Leafstem about 1" long..Strong Back

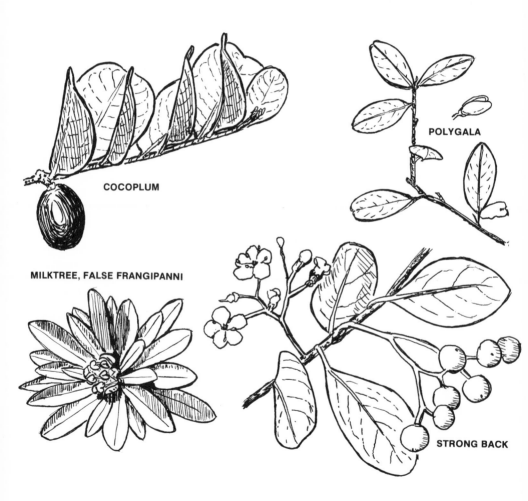

COCOPLUM

POLYGALA

MILKTREE, FALSE FRANGIPANNI

STRONG BACK

COCOPLUM
CHRYSOBALANUS ICACO

10 - 15 feet, often a shrub. **TRUNK** medium short, sometimes leaning. **CROWN** very dense, spreading; branches numerous, erect. **BARK** dark brown, thin, smooth when young; rough, flaking into long pieces with age; pink-red when cut. **TWIGS** red brown to dark brown, straight or slightly zig-zag, medium thick, slightly roughened by numerous lenticels. **LEAVES** evergreen, smooth, firm, dark green and shiny above, slightly paler below, net venation prominent; 1 1/2 - 3" long; stem very short; tip rounded, sometimes blunt pointed or notched; base rounded or wedge. **FLOWERS** in spring, sometimes off and on all year; small, numerous, pale green, on short stalked terminal clusters. **FRUIT** in summer, or off and on all year; white, pink, or black, nearly round, 1 1/2" across; a thin, rather cotton-like flesh considered sweet and edible. **FOUND** throughout the Bahamas, mainly in sandy or swampy areas; common. Florida, West Indies, Mexico, South America. Rosaceae.

POLYGALA
POLYGALA PENAEA

6 - 10 feet, often a shrub. **TRUNK** slender, short. **CROWN** rather open and sparse: branches short, erect. **BARK** light gray, smooth, thin, sometimes blotched. **TWIGS** brown, slender, smooth except for leaf scars. **LEAVES** smooth, firm, dark green and rather dull above, paler below; prominent midrib and faint net venation; 1/2 - 1" long: stem 1/4" long or less; tip blunt pointed or rounded and slightly notched; base wedge. **FLOWERS** in winter; 1/8" or less across, yellow-green, single or two on very short axillary stalk. **FRUIT** in winter and spring; about 1/4" across, flat, winged, green turning brown and drying. **FOUND** on San Salvador, South Abaco, North Andros, in low mixed broadleaf areas; very rare. Cuba. Polygalaceae.

MILK TREE
EUPHORBIA GYMNONOTA

8 - 12 feet. **TRUNK** medium, short; sap milky. **CROWN** spreading and sparse; branches slender. **BARK** gray-green to brown, thin and smooth, rougher with age. **TWIGS** gray to brown, slender, smooth. **LEAVES** often in whorls; medium firm, smooth, bright green and shiny above, paler below; venation indistinct; 1 - 3" long; stem short; tip rounded or short pointed, base narrow wedge. **FLOWERS** off and on all year; showy, bright red bracts, in short-stalked clusters at twig ends. **FRUIT** all year; light green or tinged with red, 1/3" long, rounded, 3 angled, pointed at the top. **FOUND** on San Salvador and the Southern Bahamas, in scrublands. Euphorbiaceae.

STRONG BACK
BOURRERIA OVATA

10 - 25 feet. **TRUNK** slender to medium, straight or crooked. **CROWN** irregular, somewhat spreading; branches erect, crooked. **BARK** gray-brown, thin, smooth on young trees, dark and rough in furrows with age. **TWIGS** light brown, slender, straight or crooked, smooth with numerous leaf scars. **LEAVES** smooth, medium firm, yellow-green to dark green and shiny above, slightly paler below; prominent yellow midrib, net venation; 1 1/2 - 3 1/2" long; stem 1 - 1 1/2" long; tip rounded, base wedge. **FLOWERS** in summer, occasionally off and on all year; 1/3 - 1/2" across, showy, white, numerous, in branched terminal clusters 2 - 4" long. **FRUIT** off and on all year, mainly in fall and winter; 1/3" across, globose, orange to tangerine, shiny, smooth. **FOUND** throughout the Bahamas, in mixed broadleaf areas or as a shrub in pinelands; very common in some areas. Florida, Cuba. Boraginaceae.

ALTERNATE LEAVES   WIDE TIP

5. Leafstem 1/3″ long or less
  6. Leaf base very long and narrow...Swamp Bush
  6. Leaf base wedge shape
    7. Leaves often clustered, twigs sharp ....Spiny Milk Berry
    7. Leaves not clustered, twigs not sharp
      8. Leaf thick, very firm, veins obscure................................. Box Wood
      8. Leaf thin, veins prominent ....Pigeon Berry

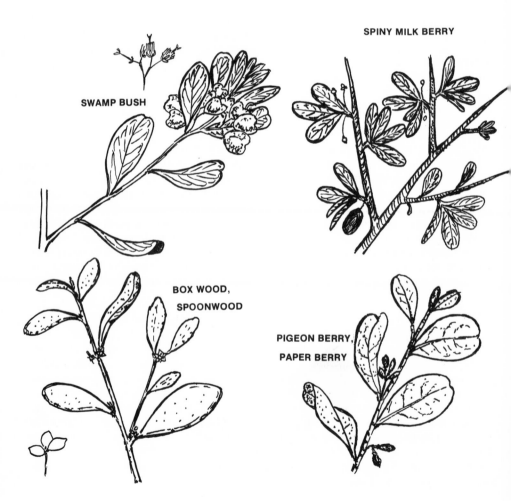

SPINY MILK BERRY

SWAMP BUSH

BOX WOOD,
SPOONWOOD

PIGEON BERRY,
PAPER BERRY

SWAMP BUSH DODONEA VISCOSA

10 - 15 feet, often a shrub. **TRUNK** very short. **CROWN** regular, spreading, medium dense; branches slender, erect, numerous. **BARK** brown, thick, rough in vertical furrows. **TWIGS** brown, slender, somewhat curved, slightly roughened by horizontal lines. **LEAVES** usually clustered at twig ends; smooth, medium firm, bright to dark green and shiny above, paler below; conspicuous net venation; 1 - 2" long; stem about 1/3" long; tip rounded, base gradually narrowed; leaf held erect; young leaves very shiny. **FLOWERS** in fall and winter; yellow-green, numerous, about 1/8" across, on short terminal stalks. **FRUIT** in winter and spring; numerous, very thin and papery, about 1/4" across, light brown (tinged with pink when immature). **FOUND** throughout the Bahamas, always in low areas. Cuba, Hispaniola. Dodonaceae.

SPINY MILK BERRY BUMELIA CELASTRINA

8 - 15 feet, or shrubby. **TRUNK** slender, short. **CROWN** irregular; branches slender, erect. **BARK** brown to dark gray, thin, rough, furrowed. **TWIGS** gray to brown, slender, smooth, with sharp ridged spines 1/4" long in the axils, single or paired. **LEAVES** often in clusters; firm, smooth, dark green and dull above and below; venation obscure; 1/2 - 1" long; stem very short; tip rounded, base narrow or wedge. **FLOWERS** in fall and winter; 1/8" long, yellow-green, fragrant, numerous, in short-stalked axillary clusters. **FRUIT** in early summer; 1/3" long, oval, purple-black, smooth, dull, edible but gummy. **FOUND** in Central Bahamas, inland, in low areas and around ponds. Florida, Cuba. Sapotaceae.

BOX WOOD MAYTENUS BUXIFOLIA

10 - 30 feet. **TRUNK** slender to medium, straight. **CROWN** narrow, medium dense; branches short, erect to horizontal. **BARK** dark brown, thick, rough in furrows. **TWIGS** gray to brown, often blotched, slender, smooth or slightly roughened by lenticels. **LEAVES** evergreen, very firm, smooth, thick, yellow-green to dark green and dull above, slightly paler below; 3/4 - 1 1/2" long; stem very short; tip rounded or blunt, base narrow or wedge, margins sometimes slightly recurved. **FLOWERS** in spring and early summer; less than .1/4" across, yellow-green, in small, short stalked clusters in leaf axils. **FRUIT** in late summer and fall; more or less round, 1/4 - 1/3" long, orange to red, smooth, splitting, shiny white flesh inside. **FOUND** throughout the Bahamas; fairly common in mixed broadleaf areas. Cuba, Hispaniola. Celastraceae.

PIGEON BERRY ERYTHROXYLUM CONFUSUM

10 - 25 feet. **TRUNK** slender, straight. **CROWN** somewhat spreading, medium dense; branches erect to horizontal. **BARK** gray to brown, thick, becoming very rough in vertical furrows with age. **TWIGS** brown, slender, straight, slightly rough. **LEAVES** smooth, thin, medium firm, bright to medium green and dull above, gray-green below, sometimes faintly areolate; prominent midrib, net venation; 1 - 1 1/2" long; stem about 1/3" long; tip rounded, often notched, base wedge. **FLOWERS** in spring and early summer; about 1/8" across, pale green, fragrant, in numerous short-stalked clusters in leaf axils and along twigs. **FRUIT** in late summer and fall; about 1/4" long, oblong, bright red, smooth, numerous. **FOUND** in Central Bahamas, but apparently not on Eleuthera, Cat Island, nor San Salvador; in mixed broadleaf areas and low swampy sites. Cuba, Jamaica. Erythroxylacaea.

ALTERNATE LEAVES   WIDE BASE   CLASPING STEM

1. Leaf usually wider than long..Seagrape
1. Leaf longer than wide
  2. Leaf widest near base
    3. Bark flaking; leaf pinnately veined... Pigeon Plum

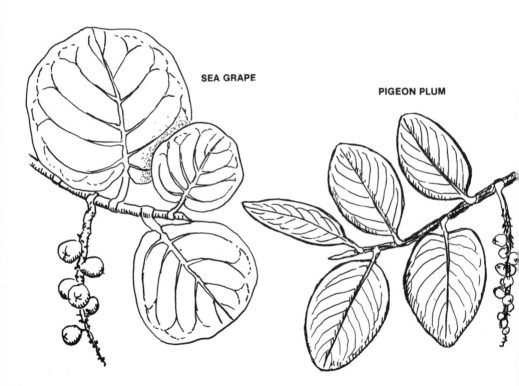

SEA GRAPE

PIGEON PLUM

SEA GRAPE — COCCOLOBA UVIFERA

15- 30 feet. **TRUNK** thick, short, often crooked. **CROWN** very spreading, generally dense; branches thick, crooked. **BARK** gray to brown, blotched, smooth, thin. **TWIGS** gray to orange-brown, thick, smooth, often with raised lenticels. **LEAVES** smooth, leathery, dark green and shiny above, slightly paler below; veins prominent, sometimes tinged with red; 4 - 5" long and 5 - 6" across; stem short, very thick; margins somewhat wavy; new growth red. **FLOWERS** in early summer; very small, numerous, white, fragrant, on long thick axillary and terminal stalks 6 - 14" long. **FRUIT** in late summer and fall; about 1/2" across, round, smooth, purple (occasionally pale green), juicy, edible, with a large seed. **FOUND** throughout the Bahamas, usually by the shore, very common. Bermuda, West Indies, Florida, Central and South America. Polygonaceae.

PIGEON PLUM — COCCOLOBA DIVERSIFOLIA

20 - 50 feet. **TRUNK** medium to thick, straight, tall. **CROWN** narrow, dense; branches erect. **BARK** light brown to gray-brown and mottled on young trees; on older ones, light brown to orange-brown, mottled, usually flaking off large thin pieces. **TWIGS** brown, sometimes mottled, medium thick, often short and crooked, more or less smooth. **LEAVES** smooth, firm, bright to dark green and shiny above, somewhat paler below; fairly prominent midrib, pinnate venation, 2 - 4" long; stem medium thick, 1/2" long or less; tip rounded or blunt, base rounded or wedge. **FLOWERS** in summer, sometimes fall; male and female on different trees; both very small, numerous, pale green, on axillary and terminal spikes 2 - 3" long. **FRUIT** in winter; about 1/3" across, numerous, round, black, dull, smooth; considered edible, a sharp, sweet taste. **FOUND** throughout the Bahamas, quite common. Florida, Jamaica, Cuba to Virgin Islands. Polygonaceae.

ALTERNATE LEAVES   WIDE BASE   CLASPING STEM

   3. Bark light gray, smooth; leaf net veined .... Bastard Pigeon Plum
2. Leaf widest near midpoint
   3. Bark smooth
      4. Venation delicate .... Boar Pigeon Plum
      4. 2 - 3 pairs of veins prominent .... Bahama Pigeon Plum
   3. Bark rough, tip of leaf irregular .... Roughbark Pigeon Plum

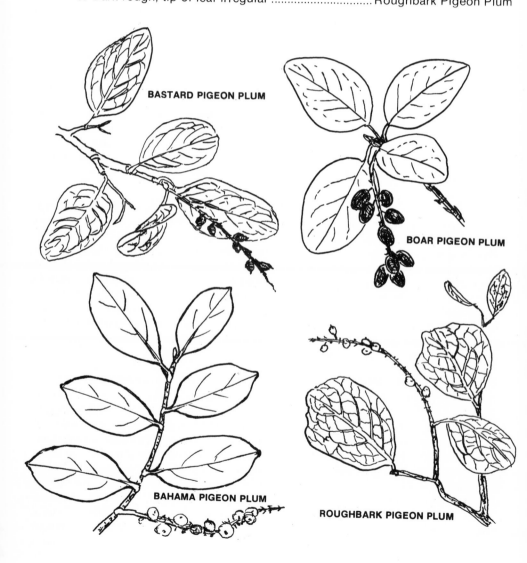

BASTARD PIGEON PLUM

BOAR PIGEON PLUM

BAHAMA PIGEON PLUM

ROUGHBARK PIGEON PLUM

BASTARD PIGEON PLUM
COCCOLOBA SWARTZII

20 - 50 feet. **TRUNK** medium, tall, straight. **CROWN** narrow, dense; branches erect. **BARK** light gray, sometimes mottled with black, smooth, thin, darkening and roughening with age from the base up. **TWIGS** gray to light brown, sometimes mottled, medium thick, crooked, smooth but for a few leaf scars. **LEAVES** smooth, medium firm, dark green and shiny above, slightly paler below, sometimes covered with rusty spots; net venation; 1 1/2 - 4" long; stem medium thick, 1/2" long or less; tip rounded or blunt, base wedge or rounded. **FLOWERS** mainly in summer, sometimes in fall; male and female on different trees; both very small, numerous, pale green, on curved axillary or terminal spikes 3 - 4" long. **FRUIT** in fall and winter; 1/4" long or less; ovoid, black, smooth, numerous. **FOUND** throughout the Bahamas, rather common in most areas. Cuba. Polygonaceae.

BOAR PIGEON PLUM
COCCOLOBA KRUGII

10 - 20 feet. **TRUNK** slender, short to medium tall. **CROWN** narrow and medium dense, sometimes very open; branches erect, sometimes straggling. **BARK** gray-brown, usually blotched, smooth, thin, rough in vertical furrows with age. **TWIGS** gray-brown, slender to medium, crooked, roughened by leaf scars and lenticels. **LEAVES** firm, smooth, dark green and shiny above, slightly paler below; delicate but definite pinnate venation; 1 - 3" long; midrib sometimes red; stem about 1/3" long; tip rounded or blunt pointed, base rounded or slightly cordate. **FLOWERS** in summer and fall; male and female on different trees; very small, white, on axillary or terminal spike 1 - 2 1/2" long. **FRUIT** in fall and winter; under 1/4" long, ovoid, smooth, dark red. **FOUND** throughout the Bahamas, in scrublands and mixed broadleaf areas. A cross with C. uvifera has been found on Abaco. Jamaica, Puerto Rico, Barbuda. Polygonaceae.

BAHAMAS PIGEON PLUM
COCCOLOBA TENUIFOLIA

10 - 15 feet, usually a shrub. **TRUNK** slender, short. **CROWN** rather narrow, sparse to medium dense; branches slender, erect. **BARK** brown, generally mottled, smooth, thin. **TWIGS** gray-brown, slender, short, straight or a bit curved, smooth or slightly rough. **LEAVES** firm, smooth, bright to dark green and shiny above, slightly paler below; midrib prominent, 2 - 3 pairs of veins very prominent; 1 - 3" long; stem 1/4" long or less; tip blunt pointed, base wedge. **FLOWERS** in summer; male and female on different trees; very small, white, numerous, on terminal or axillary stalks 2 - 5" long, generally drooping. **FRUIT** in winter; small, ovoid, about 1/4" long, black, smooth. **FOUND** in Central and Southern Bahamas, in scrubland or mixed broadleaf areas. A natural hybrid between the above and C. uvifera has been found. Polygonaceae.

ROUGHBARK PIGEON PLUM
COCCOLOBA NORTHROPIAE

10 - 20 feet. **TRUNK** slender to medium, straight. **CROWN** narrow, open and sparse on young trees, more spreading and dense on mature ones. **BARK** gray, occasionally blotched, thin, rough, cracking into small plates. **TWIGS** gray to gray-brown, slender, zig-zag or twisted, slightly roughened by raised horizontal lines. **LEAVES** smooth, firm, bright green and shiny above, slightly paler below; prominent yellow midrib, net venation; 1 - 3" long; stem 1/4" long or less; tip blunt or rounded, base wedge or rounded. **FLOWERS** in spring and summer; male and female on different trees; both small, white, nearly stemless, numerous on axillary and terminal spikes 2 - 3" long. **FRUIT** in summer and fall; about 1/4" long, round, red to black, shiny, smooth. **FOUND** in Central Bahamas, usually in scrublands where it does not attain tree size; occasionally in mixed broadleaf areas, consderably bigger. The least of the Coccolobas, and the only one with rough gray bark. Cuba. Polygonaceae.

ALTERNATE LEAVES   WIDE BASE   ROLLED BUD LEAF

1. Leaf margin not recurved; fruit stalkless .... Golden Wild Fig
1. Leaf margin usually recurved; fruit stalked
   2. Leaf pendent, 2 - 4″ long, bark brown .... Short-Leaf Wild Fig
   2. Leaf 1 - 2″ long, bark gray .... Small-Leaf Wild Fig
1. Leaf about 2″ long
   2. Leaf yellow-green, stiff, short pointed .... Buttonwood

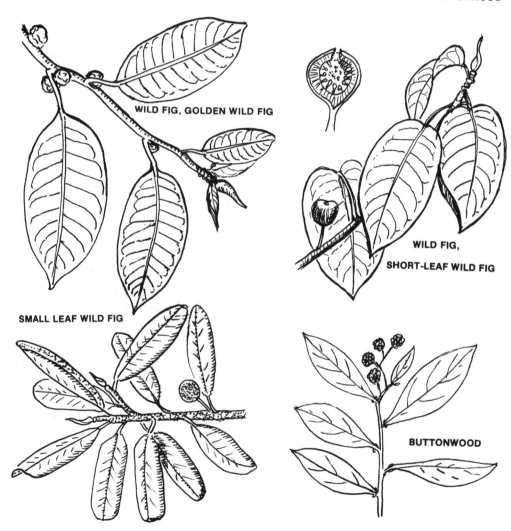

WILD FIG, GOLDEN WILD FIG

WILD FIG, SHORT-LEAF WILD FIG

SMALL LEAF WILD FIG

BUTTONWOOD

GOLDEN WILD FIG   FICUS AUREA
20 - 50 feet. **TRUNK** thick, short, often divided into several secondary trunks. **CROWN** very spreading, generally dense; branches large, horizontal to erect, often with aerial roots. **BARK** light gray to nearly black, thin, smooth, occasionally breaking into small plates; bleeds white latex when cut. **TWIGS** red-brown to brown, straight to slightly zig-zag, thick, smooth with occasional lenticels; bleed white latex when broken. **LEAVES** firm, smooth, dark green and shiny above, paler below; pinnate venation, midrib promi-nent; 2 - 5" long, stem thick, 1" long or more; tip short pointed or rounded, base wedge, sometimes unequal. **FLOWERS** off and on all year, inside small, round, fleshy con-tainers. **FRUIT** off and on all year; 1/3 - 1/2" across, globose, dark red, stalkless, singly or 2 - 3 in leaf axils, with numerous seeds; edible. **FOUND** in Northern and Central Bahamas, common in mixed broadleaf areas, usually stunted in pinelands and scrub-lands. (Short-leaf Wild Fig has longer leafstems and leaves that are rounded at the base.) Florida, Cuba, Hispaniola, Jamaica. Moraceae.

SHORT LEAF FIG   FICUS CITRIFOLIA
20 to 40 feet. **TRUNK** thick, short, often divided into secondary trunks. **CROWN** broad, spreading, medium dense; branches large, erect, often with aerial roots. **BARK** pale gray to dark brown, smooth on young trees but rough and breaking into small plates with age; bleeds white latex when cut. **TWIGS** red-brown to dark brown, thick, gener-ally straight, smooth with scattered lenticels; bleed white latex when cut. **LEAVES** firm, smooth, dark green and shiny above, paler below; venation pinnate, midrib prominent; 2 - 4" long; stem 1 1/2" long or more; tip short pointed or rounded, base rounded, margins often recurved; leaves always pendent. **FLOWERS** off and on all year; globose, about 1/3 - 1/2" across, dark red, single or 2 or 3 in a leaf axil, on a stalk about 1/4" long; numerous small white seeds; edible. **FOUND** throughout the Bahamas, quite common; a smaller tree than F. aurea. Florida, Cuba, San Domingo. Moraceae.

SMALL LEAF FIG   FICUS PERFORATA
20 - 40 feet. **TRUNK** thick, short, often with secondary roots, rarely multiple. **CROWN** broad, spreading, usually regular; branches medium, numerous, erect to horizontal. **BARK** light gray, thin, smooth; bleeds white latex when cut. **TWIGS** gray, firm, slender, straight, smooth; bleed white latex when cut. **LEAVES** smooth, firm, medium to dark green and shiny above, paler and with a prominent midrib below; 1 - 2" long; stem short; tip short pointed, rounded, or blunt; base wedge or rounded; margins usually recurved. **FLOWERS** off and on all year; very small, formed inside round fleshy containers. **FRUIT** off and on all year; numerous, round, red-brown, 1/4" across or less, on stalk 1/4" long, single in leaf axils. **FOUND** in Northern and Central Bahamas, in mixed broadleaf areas. Cuba. Moraceae.

BUTTONWOOD   CONOCARPUS ERECTUS
15 - 35 feet. **TRUNK** medium to thick, sometimes crooked. **CROWN** irregular, often spreading, sometimes rather narrow; branches twisted, numerous. **BARK** gray-brown, thick, very rough in furrows. **TWIGS** brown, thick, very stiff, somewhat roughened by numerous leaf scars. **LEAVES** smooth, stiff, yellow-green and shiny above and below; venation not prominent; 1 - 2 1/4" long; stem about 1/2" long, often heavily tinged with dark red; tip short pointed, blunt, or rounded, base narrow or wedge. **FLOWERS** off and on all year; minute, in dense round heads about 1/3" across, pale green, on axillary or terminal stalks about 1" long. **FRUIT** off and on all year; about 1/2" across, more or less round, brown and cone-like. **FOUND** throughout the Bahamas, along the coast and in marshy areas. A common variety, Silver Buttonwood (C. erectus var. sericeus) has leaves covered with silvery down, an excellent ornamental. Bermuda, Florida, West Indies, tropical South America. Combretaceae.

ALTERNATE LEAVES   WIDE BASE   LEAF SLENDER

  2. Leaf bright to dark green, firm, long pointed or rounded
    3. Leaf tip rounded or blunt..White Beefwood
    3. Leaf tip sharp, long pointed ....Gulf Graytwig
1. Leaf usually more than 2" long
  2. Veins obscure, leaf usually twisted..Bontia
  2. Veins noticeable, leaf usually not twisted
    3. Base of leaf rounded
      4. Leaf dark green, veins prominent ....Guiana Plum

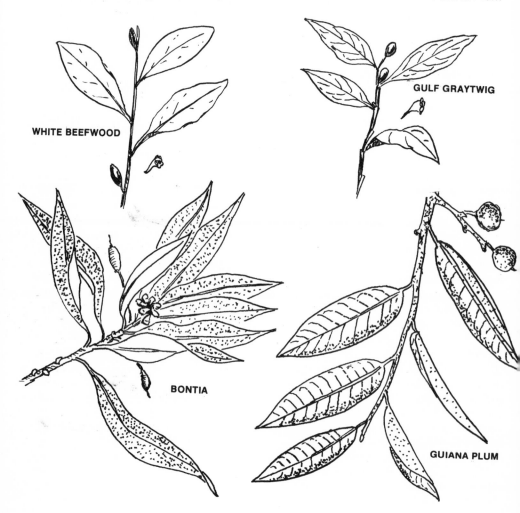

WHITE BEEFWOOD

GULF GRAYTWIG

BONTIA

GUIANA PLUM

WHITE BEEFWOOD   SCHOEPFIA OBOVATA

10 - 20 feet. **TRUNK** slender to medium, straight or crooked. **CROWN** regular and narrow, medium dense; branches twisted, horizontal or drooping. **BARK** gray to brown, thick, rough in vertical furrows. **TWIGS** gray, often mottled, slender, smooth, sometimes dark red at the ends. **LEAVES** firm, smooth, bright to dark green and shiny above, dull below; venation indistinct; 1 - 1 1/2" long; stem very short; tip blunt pointed or rounded, base wedge, margins often slightly to strongly waved; leaves dark red when young. **FLOWERS** off and on all year, mainly winter and spring; less than 1/4" across, green heavily tinged with red, single or few in short-stalked terminal clusters. **FRUIT** off and on all year, mainly winter and spring; about 1/3" long, almost round, bright to dark red, smooth, shiny. **FOUND** throughout the Bahamas, but not on Inagua; in mixed broadleaf areas. Cuba, Hispaniola, Puerto Rico. Olacaceae.

GULF GRAYTWIG   SCHOEPFIA CHRYSOPHYLLOIDES

10 - 20 feet. **TRUNK** slender, straight. **CROWN** somewhat spreading and irregular; branches horizontal or erect, numerous, crooked. **BARK** light gray, smooth, thin, becoming darker and rough in furrows with age. **TWIGS** pale gray, zig-zag, slender, smooth. **LEAVES** smooth, medium firm, bright green and shiny above, paler below; venation not prominent; 1 - 2 1/2" long; stem about 1/4" long; tip long pointed, base wedge, margins wavy; new growth red. **FLOWERS** in fall and early winter; 1/8" or less across, red-green, single or in small short-stalked axillary or terminal clusters. **FRUIT** in winter; oval, about 1/4" across, red, smooth, shiny. **FOUND** in Northern and Central Bahamas, but apparently not on New Providence, Cat Island, nor San Salvador; in mixed broadleaf areas, not common. Florida, Cuba, Jamaica. Olacaceae.

BONTIA   BONTIA DAPHNOIDES

10 - 15 feet. **TRUNK** slender, short, sometimes multiple. **CROWN** spreading, medium dense; branches medium, erect. **BARK** light brown, thin, somewhat rough on mature trees. **TWIGS** light brown, slender, straight or curved, smooth, with numerous leaf scars. **LEAVES** smooth, firm, dark green to yellow-green and slightly shiny above, paler below; 2 - 4" long; midrib prominent; stem rather thick, about 1/2" long; tip long-pointed, base wedge or narrow, margins generally recurved; entire leaf often twisted. **FLOWERS** off and on all year; about 1" long, 1/3" wide, yellow-brown with a purple lip; usually solitary on short axillary stalk. **FRUIT** off and on all year; yellow, pear-shape, about 1/2" long, turning brown and drying; a thin covering of flesh over a hard seed. **FOUND** on Exuma, Cat Island, Inagua, in mixed broadleaf areas; not common. Cuba, Guianas. Myoporaceae.

GUIANA PLUM   DRYPETES LATERIFLORA

10 - 20 feet. **TRUNK** slender, short. **CROWN** somewhat spreading, irregular; branches short, erect. **BARK** light gray to light brown, smooth, thin. **TWIGS** gray, slender, straight, slightly roughened by numerous leaf scars. **LEAVES** firm, smooth, dark green and shiny above, slightly paler below; net venation prominent; 2 - 4" long; stem 1/2" long or less; tip long pointed, base wedge. **FLOWERS** in winter; male and female on different trees; male very small, numerous, on short stalks in leaf axils; females single or few. **FRUIT** in spring or early summer; more or less globose, 1/4 - 1/3" across, orange-red, slightly downy. **FOUND** on Abaco, Andros, New Providence, but it is neither common nor outstanding; net venation distinguishes it from Ilex krugiana and Nectandra coriacea. Florida, Cuba, Hispaniola, Jamaica. Euphorbiaceae.

ALTERNATE LEAVES   WIDE BASE   LEAF SLENDER

    4. Leaf light green, veins not prominent ....Bahama Cestrum
3. Base of leaf wedge shape
    4. Leaf tip very long pointed, stem 1" long....................................Lancewood
    4. Leaf tip pointed, leafstem 1/2" long
      5. Leaf gray and downy below, twig gray-downy ....Swamp Bay
      5. Leaf green, not downy; twig rusty-downy ....Cassada Wood

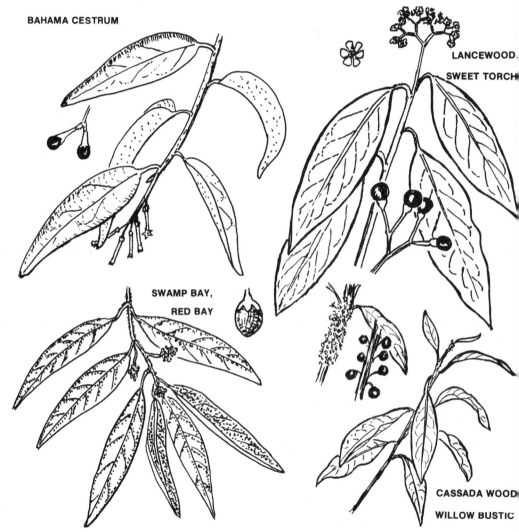

BAHAMA CESTRUM

LANCEWOOD

SWEET TORCH

SWAMP BAY,

RED BAY

CASSADA WOOD

WILLOW BUSTIC

CESTRUM   CESTRUM BAHAMENSE

8 - 10 feet, usually a shrub. **TRUNK** short. **CROWN** somewhat spreading, very open; branches slender, drooping, as a shrub, but rather dense and compact when a tree. **BARK** gray to light brown, thin, slightly roughened by fine horizontal lines and lenticels. **LEAVES** thin, medium firm to firm, smooth, bright green to yellow-green and shiny above, paler below; fine net venation; 2 - 4" long; stem 1/2" long or more; tip long or short pointed, base wedge, margins somewhat wavy. **FLOWERS** in winter and spring; pale green, about 1/2" long, very slender, numerous, in few-flowered axillary or terminal clusters. **FRUIT** in spring and early summer; about 1/2" long, ovoid, dark purple to black, smooth, shiny, seated in a prominent calyx. **FOUND** in Northern and Central Bahamas, but apparently not on Cat Island nor San Salvador; usually in pine forests; not common. Cuban keys. Solanaceae.

LANCEWOOD   NECTANDRA CORIACEA

15 - 30 feet. **TRUNK** slender to medium, straight, short. **CROWN** spreading, very dense; branches erect, numerous. **BARK** dark gray to brown, thin, smooth, sometimes mottled. **TWIGS** gray, slender, straight, smooth, with occasional leaf scars; aromatic when crushed. **LEAVES** firm, smooth, dark green and shiny above, paler below; midrib prominent, net venation; 3 - 6" long; stem 1" long or less; tip very long pointed, base wedge or narrow; aromatic when crushed. **FLOWERS** in late spring to mid-summer; about 1/4" across, white, very fragrant, numerous in large clusters at twig ends. **FRUIT** in fall and winter; about 1/2" long, ovate, blue-black, smooth, shiny, seated in prominent yellow or red calyx. **FOUND** throughout the Bahamas, but apparently not on Inagua nor Mayaguana; very common in mixed broadleaf areas. Florida, West Indies. Lauraceae.

SWAMP BAY   PERSEA PALUSTRIS

10 - 20 feet. **TRUNK** slender to medium, short. **CROWN** spreading, medium dense; branches erect. **BARK** brown, thick, rough, fissured. **TWIGS** firm, smooth, yellow-green and shiny above, gray-green and downy below; prominent midrib, net venation; 3 - 5" long; stem about 1/2" long; tip pointed, base wedge. **FLOWERS** in spring; pale green, small, singly or in small groups in the axils, on stalks 1" long or more. **FRUIT** in summer; green, turning dark blue, shiny, smooth, ovoid, about 1/3" long, seated in a prominent calyx. **FOUND** on Grand Bahama and Abaco, around ponds and swamps; uncommon. Virginia to Florida. Lauraceae.

CASSADA WOOD   BUMELIA SALICIFOLIA

20 - 50 feet. **TRUNK** medium to thick, tall, straight. **CROWN** somewhat spreading, dense; branches erect. **BARK** brown to gray-brown, thin, rough in furrows; inner layer red. **TWIGS** brown, straight, slender, smooth, with scattered leaf scars; new growth green-brown and hairy. **LEAVES** smooth, medium firm, yellow-green to dark green and shiny above, paler below; pinnate venation; 2 - 4" long; stem about 1/2" long; tip long or short pointed, base narrow or wedge, margins usually wavy. **FLOWERS** in late winter and spring; about 1/4" across, yellow, numerous, fragrant, in very short-stalked clusters along the twigs. **FRUIT** in summer; 1/3" across, black, smooth, shiny, gummy, not considered edible. **FOUND** throughout the Bahamas, in mixed broadleaf areas or as a shrub in pinelands; very common. Florida, Cuba, West Indies, Jamaica, Mexico. Sapotaceae.

ALTERNATE LEAVES   WIDE BASE   LEAF BROAD

1. Leaf tip sharp pointed
   2. Leaf base wedge shape.. White Wood
   2. Leaf base broad
     3. Leaf surface dull, midrib silver-brown................................Sweet Wood Bark
     3. Leaf surface shiny
       4. Leaf 3 - 5" long, tree grows in wetlands.....................................Pond Apple
       4. Leaf less than 3 - 5" long, tree on dry land
         5. Midrib thick, twig gray-green ....Krug's Holly

WHITE WOOD,
GUANA BERRY

SWEET WOOD BARK,
CASCARILLA

POND APPLE

KRUG'S HOLLY

WHITE WOOD   DRYPETES DIVERSIFOLIA

15 - 30 feet. **TRUNK** slender to medium, straight. **CROWN** narrow, medium dense;
branches short, erect to horizontal. **BARK** light gray, heavily blotched with black,
smooth, thick. **TWIGS** light gray, straight or slightly zig-zag, rather stiff, medium thick,
roughened by numerous lenticels. **LEAVES** evergreen, smooth, very stiff, dark to very
dark green and shiny above, slightly paler below; net venation; shape variable, midrib
often skewed, some young leaves with marginal spines; 2 - 4" long; stem thick, about
1/4" long; tip short or long pointed or rounded, base rounded, margins smooth and
slightly thickened. **FLOWERS** in early summer; male and female on different trees; both
small, yellow-green; males in dense short-stalked clusters, females single or in small
groups in leaf axils. **FRUIT** in fall or early winter; almost round, about 1/2" long, green
turning white, velvety. **FOUND** throughout the Bahamas, in mixed broadleaf areas,
sometimes near the shore. Florida. Euphorbiaceae.

SWEET WOOD BARK..   CROTON ELUTERIA

10 - 20 feet. **TRUNK** slender, straight. **CROWN** regular, not dense; branches slender,
erect. **BARK** light gray, sometimes blotched gray-black; thin, more or less smooth; aromatic when cut. **TWIGS** slender, smooth, brown becoming gray, straight but usually
curved towards the end. **LEAVES** smooth, medium firm, light green and rather dull
above, much paler below with numerous tiny silver-brown dots; midrib silver-brown
and prominent, venation pinnate; 1 - 2 1/2" long; stem brown, 1" long or less; tip very
short pointed, base rounded or semi-heart shaped, margins serrate; strongly aromatic
when crushed. **FLOWERS** mostly in spring; white, very small, numerous, on terminal
spikes about 1" long. **FRUIT** off and on all year, mostly in summer; about 1/3" long,
more or less round, gray-green, dull. **FOUND** in Central and Southern Bahamas, in
mixed broadleaf areas; becoming rare due to use of bark in liqueurs. Euphorbiaceae.

POND APPLE   ANNONA GLABRA

10 - 20 feet. **TRUNK** thick, short, base swollen, sometimes buttressed. **CROWN** spreading, medium dense; branches twisted, erect or horizontal. **BARK** dark brown, thick,
rough in fissures. **TWIGS** green to brown, short, slender, smooth. **LEAVES** firm,
smooth, dark green and shiny above, paler below; midrib prominent, venation reticulate; 3 - 5" long; stem about 1/3" long; tip long or short pointed, base rounded or
wedge· leaf aromatic when crushed. **FLOWERS** in spring; showy, about 1" across,
petals rather thick, cream-white with red blotch on inner side, solitary on stout, drooping stalk. **FRUIT** in summer and fall; smooth and somewhat shiny with a coarse network
of veins; heart-shape; 3 - 5" across, yellow-green blotched with light brown; edible, but
pulp very mealy. **FOUND** in Northern and Central Bahamas, in low or wet ground or in
pot holes. Florida, West Indies, Northern South America. Annonaceae.

KRUG'S HOLLY   ILEX KRUGIANA

15 - 35 feet. **TRUNK** slender to medium, straight. **CROWN** somewhat spreading, dense,
regular; branches erect. **BARK** light gray, smooth, thin. **TWIGS** green to gray, slender,
straight, smooth, with occasional lenticels. **LEAVES** evergreen, firm, smooth, dark
green and shiny above, slightly paler below; midrib thick, venation not prominent; 1 1/2
- 3" long; stem about 1" long; tip long or blunt pointed, base wedge, margin often wavy.
FLOWERS in spring and early summer; small, white, in short-stalked axillary clusters,
numerous. **FRUIT** in summer; about 1/4" across, round, numerous, showy, dark red
turning amost black. **FOUND** in Northern and Central Bahamas, in mixed broadleaf
areas. Closely resembles Drypetes lateriflora, but has longer stem and less prominent
venation. Florida, Hispaniola. Aquifoliaceae.

ALTERNATE LEAVES   WIDE BASE   LEAF BROAD

    5. Midrib thin, twig brown..Laurel Cherry
1. Leaf tip blunt or notched
  2. Stem long, 1" or more
    3. Veins parallel, indistinct...Sapodilla
    3. Veins net, prominent
      4. Leaf to 6" long, margins wavy...Mastic
      4 Leaf to 3 1/2" long margins not wavy.........................Strong Back

**WEST INDIAN
LAUREL CHERRY**

SAPODILLA

MASTIC

STRONG BACK

LAUREL CHERRY
PRUNUS MYRTIFOLIA

10 - 20 feet. **TRUNK** slender to medium, straight. **CROWN** rather narrow, medium dense; branches erect to horizontal. **BARK** brown, thin, smooth, slightly cracked with age. **TWIGS** brown, slender, straight or zig-zag, smooth except for numerous lenticels. **LEAVES** smooth, medium firm, dark green and shiny above, paler below; net venation; 2 - 4" long; stem about 1/3" long; tip long pointed, base wedge or rounded, margins wavy; odor reminiscent of almonds when crushed. **FLOWERS** in winter and spring; small, white, numerous, on axillary stalks 1" long or more. **FRUIT** in summer and fall; about 1/3" across; almost round, smooth, dark blue, nearly black. **FOUND** on Grand Bahama, Abaco, and Andros; usually an understory tree in mixed broadleaf areas. Florida, Jamaica, Cuba, Hispaniola. Rosaceae.

SAPODILLA
MANILKARA ZAPOTA

20 - 50 feet. **TRUNK** thick, straight, rather short; bleeds latex when cut. **CROWN** spreading, dense; branches horizontal, numerous. **BARK** dark brown, very thick and rough in vertical furrows. **TWIGS** brown, thick, short, straight or slightly curved, roughened by lenticels and old leaf scars; bleed latex when broken. **LEAVES** clustered at twig ends; smooth, firm, dark green and somewhat shiny above, slightly paler below; midrib prominent, venation obscure; 2 - 5" long; stem about 1" long and rather thick; tip blunt, often notched, base wedge; bleed latex when crushed. **FLOWERS** off and on all year, mainly in winter and spring; about 3/4" across, white with brown calyx, solitary on 1" stalk at twig ends. **FRUIT** off and on all year, mainly in spring and ummer; about 3" long, 2 - 3" across, almost round, brown, somewhat rough, sweet, edible; several shiny black seeds 3/4" long. **FOUND** through the Bahamas, moderately common in mixed broadleaf areas and in cultivation. An early introduction from Central America, now gone wild. Sapotaceae.

MASTIC
MASTICHODENDRON FOETIDISSIMUM

, 20 - 50 feet. **TRUNK** medium to thick, straight, tall. **CROWN** spreading, dense, usually rounded; branches medium to thick, horizontal to erect. **BARK** brown to gray-brown, thick, somewhat rough, cracking into small pieces with age. **TWIGS** gray-brown, straight or curved, thick, smooth but for numerous leaf scars. **LEAVES** smooth, firm, dark to very dark green and shiny above, paler below; very prominent midrib, pinnate venation; 2 - 6" long; stem 1" long or more; tip rounded, sometimes notched; base rounded, sometimes unequal; margins usually very wavy. **FLOWERS** in summer; about 1/4" across, numerous, pale yellow, strongly scented, short-stalked, in small clusters along the twigs and in the axils. **FRUIT** in spring and early summer; about 1" long, orange-yellow, oval, smooth, very gummy. **FOUND** throughout the Bahamas, in mixed broadleaf areas or stunted in pine forests. Florida, Jamaica, Cuba to Barbadoes. Sapotaceae.

STRONG BACK..
BOURRERIA OVATA

10 - 25 feet. **TRUNK** slender to medium, straight or crooked. **CROWN** irregular, somewhat spreading; branches erect, crooked. **BARK** gray-brown, thin, smooth on young trees, dark and rough in furrows with age. **TWIGS** light brown, slender, straight or crooked, smooth with numerous leaf scars. **LEAVES** smooth, medium firm, yellow-green to dark green and shiny above, slightly paler below; prominent yellow midrib, net venation; 1 1/2 - 3 1/2" long; stem 1 - 1 1/2" long; tip rounded, base wedge. **FLOWERS** in summer, occasionally off and on all year; 1/3 - 1/2" across, showy, white, numerous, in branched terminal clusters 2 - 4" long. **FRUIT** off and on all year, mainly in fall and winter; 1/3" across, globose, orange to tangerine, shiny, smooth. **FOUND** throughout the Bahamas, in mixed broadleaf areas or as a shrub in pinelands; very common in some areas. Florida, Cuba. Boraginaceae.

ALTERNATE LEAVES   WIDE BASE   LEAF BROAD

2. Stem short, 1/2" long or less
  3. Leaf surface dull
    4. Leaf short, 1" long or less ....Polygala

    4. Leaf longer than 1"
      [5] Leaf stiff
      6. Leaf surface rough, veins net...Featherbed
      6. Leaf surface smooth, parallel veins...Wild Dilly
    5. Leaf soft, flexible
      6. Leaf areolate (see text) ....Pigeon Berry

FEATHER BED, **BOA WOOD**

POLYGALA

WILD DILLY,
WILD SAPODILLA

PIGEON BERRY, PAPER BERRY

POLYGALA   POLYGALA PENAEA

6 - 10 feet, often a shrub. **TRUNK** slender, short. **CROWN** rather open and sparse:
branches short, erect. **BARK** light gray, smooth, thin, sometimes blotched. **TWIGS**
brown, slender, smooth except for leaf scars. **LEAVES** smooth, firm, dark green and
rather dull above, paler below; prominent midrib and faint net venation: 1/2 - 1" long:
stem 1/4" long or less; tip blunt pointed or rounded and slightly notched; base wedge.
FLOWERS in winter; 1/8" or less across, yellow-green, single or two on very short axillary stalk. **FRUIT** in winter and spring; about 1/4" across, flat, winged, green turning
brown and drying. **FOUND** on San Salvador, South Abaco. North Andros. in low mixed
broadleaf areas; very rare. Cuba. Polygalaceae.

FEATHERBED   DIOSPYROS CRASSINERVIS

10 - 20 feet, more often a shrub. **TRUNK** slender to medium, straight. **CROWN** irregular
and sparse as a shrub, more regular and dense as a tree; branches erect. **BARK** brown.
thin, smooth. **TWIGS** gray to brown, slender, very stiff, straight, roughened by horizontal lines and leaf scars. **LEAVES** very stiff and rough, dark green and dull above,
paler and less rough below; prominent midrib, net venation conspicuous; 1 - 3" long;
stem thick, 1/4" long or less; tip rounded or blunt, base rounded or wedge. **FLOWERS** in
fall; male and female on different trees, both very small; male in short-stalked axillary
clusters, female solitary, almost stalkless. **FRUIT** in late winter and spring; globose.
about 1" across, black, smooth. **FOUND** in Central and Southern Bahamas, but apparently not on Inagua; a shrub in pine forests and a tree in mixed broadleaf areas. Cuba.
Hispaniola. Ebenaceae.

WILD DILLY   MANILKARA BAHAMENSIS

10 - 20 feet. **TRUNK** medium to thick, short, often crooked; bleeds white latex when cut.
CROWN spreading, dense; branches horizontal, numerous. **BARK** light gray to brown,
thick, rough, cracking into small pieces. **TWIGS** brown, thick smooth, with occasional
leaf scars; bleed white latex when cut. **LEAVES** clustered at twig ends; firm, smooth.
dark green and faintly shiny above, paler below; midrib prominent, many fine parallel
veins; 2 - 4" long; stem rusty brown, about 1/2" long; tip rounded or notched, base
rounded or unequal; leaves bleed white latex when crushed. **FLOWERS** all year, mainly
spring and summer; about 1/2" across, light yellow, in pendent axillary clusters. **FRUIT**
all year, mainly summer and fall; 3/4 - 1" across; round, brown, a small spike at the apex;
bleeds white latex when young; when ripe, edible but gummy. **FOUND** through the
Bahamas, commonly along the shore, sometimes inland. Florida, Cuba. Sapotaceae.

PIGEON BERRY   ERYTHROXYLUM AREOLATUM

10 - 25 feet. **TRUNK** slender, straight. **CROWN** narrow, medium dense; branches very
erect. **BARK** brown to red-brown, sometimes blotched; smooth and thin when young.
somewhat rough, in small plates, with age. **TWIGS** brown to red-brown, slender.
straight, slightly roughened in horizontal lines. **LEAVES** thin, medium firm, smooth.
dark green and dull above, paler below; midrib outstanding, venation net; two faint.
slightly curved lines (areolate) on each side of the midrib; 2 - 4" long; stem about 1/3"
long; tip notched or blunt, base wedge. **FLOWERS** in spring or early summer: very
small, pale green, in numerous short-stalked axillary clusters. **FRUIT** in late summer
and fall; about 1 - 4" long, oblong, bright red, smooth, shiny, numerous. **FOUND** in
Northern and Central Bahamas and Long Island, in mixed broadleaf areas. Cuba to
Puerto Rico, Jamaica, Colombia. Erythroxylaceae.

ALTERNATE LEAVES   WIDE BASE   LEAF BROAD

     6. Leaf not areolate...Soldier Wood
3. Leaf shiny
  4. Leaf tip tapering
    5. Leaf very shiny, venation prominent ....Bull Wood
    5. Leaf slightly shiny, venation obscure..Marl Berry

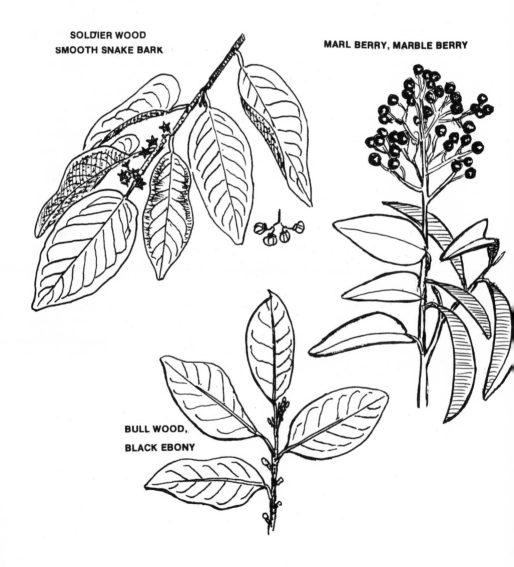

SOLDIER WOOD
SMOOTH SNAKE BARK

MARL BERRY, MARBLE BERRY

BULL WOOD,
BLACK EBONY

SOLDIER WOOD
COLUBRINA ELLIPTICA

10 - 20 feet. **TRUNK** slender, straight. **CROWN** somewhat spreading and regular; branches erect. **BARK** brown, blotched, thin, flaking. **TWIGS** gray to brown, smooth, slender, with some lenticels. **LEAVES** smooth, thin, rather flexible, dark green and dull above, paler below; midrib prominent, venation pinnate; 1 - 3″ long; stem slender, 1/2″ long or less; tip short pointed, base rounded or wedge. **FLOWERS** in spring, sometimes in fall; very small, yellow-green, in very short-stalked clusters in leaf axils. **FRUIT** in fall, sometimes winter or spring; smooth, dull orange, more or less round, about 1/4″ across, with very small shiny black seeds. **FOUND** on Eleuthera and Andros, not common; in low (more rarely high) mixed broadleaf areas. Florida, Jamaica, Cuba to Martinique. Rhamnaceae.

BULL WOOD
PERA BUMELIIFOLIA

15 - 35 feet. **TRUNK** slender to medium, straight, sometimes with swellings. **CROWN** somewhat spreading, usually regular, medium dense; branches horizontal to erect. **BARK** gray-brown, often mottled, smooth and thin, becoming somewhat roughened with age. **TWIGS** gray, slender, straight or zig-zag, slightly roughened by horizontal lines and numerous leaf scars. **LEAVES** medium firm, smooth, dark green and very shiny above, paler below; midvein rather prominent, net venation; 2 - 3″ long; stem 1/2″ long; tip blunt or rounded, sometimes notched, base usually wedge, margins wavy and somewhat recurved. **FLOWERS** in spring and early summer; male and female on different trees; male very small, cream coloured, almost round, numerous on short stalks in leaf axils; female single or few. **FRUIT** in summer; olive-shape, about 1/2″ long, green turning dark brown, red pulp around a few black seeds. **FOUND** on Abaco, Andros, and New Providence, in mixed broadleaf areas. Cuba. Euphorbiaceae.

MARLBERRY
ARDISIA ESCALLONIOIDES

10 - 20 feet. **TRUNK** slender, straight. **CROWN** narrow, medium dense; branches erect. **BARK** gray, smooth, thin. **TWIGS** brown to red-brown, slender to medium, straight or slightly curved, smooth but for leaf scars. **LEAVES** firm, smooth, yellow-green to dark green and shiny above, paler below; venation inconspicuous; 1 1/2 - 4″ long; stem thick, about 1/4″ long; tip blunt pointed, base wedge or sometimes unequal, margins recurved. **FLOWERS** in fall, occasionally summer; about 1/4″ long, white, with yellow stamems, fragrant, numerous on branched terminal stalks 3″ long or more. **FRUIT** in winter, occasionally in spring; about 1/3″ across, globose, black, numerous, shiny, smooth, sour tasting. **FOUND** in Northern and Central Bahamas, common in mixed broadleaf areas; good food for birds. Mrysinaceae.

ALTERNATE LEAVES   WIDE BASE   LEAF BROAD

4. Leaf tip broadly blunt or notched
   5. Leaf very stiff, midrib often skewed.......................................White Wood
   5. Leaf firm, midrib straight
      6. Leaves crowded along twig, stem short ....Cocoplum
      6. Leaves spaced, not crowded; stem 1/4" ....Milk Berry

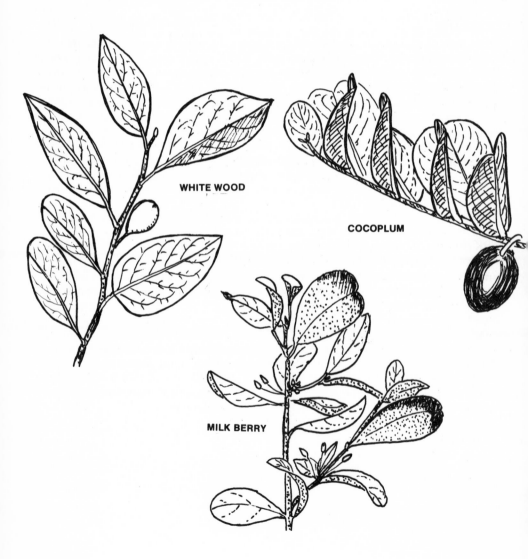

WHITE WOOD

COCOPLUM

MILK BERRY

WHITE WOOD   DRYPETES DIVERSIFOLIA

15 - 30 feet. **TRUNK** slender to medium, straight. **CROWN** narrow, medium dense; branches short, erect to horizontal. **BARK** light gray, heavily blotched with black, smooth, thick. **TWIGS** light gray, straight or slightly zig-zag, rather stiff, medium thick, roughened by numerous lenticels. **LEAVES** evergreen, smooth, very stiff, dark to very dark green and shiny above, slightly paler below; net venation; shape variable, midrib often skewed, some young leaves with marginal spines; 2 - 4" long; stem thick, about 1/4" long; tip short or long pointed or rounded, base rounded, margins smooth and slightly thickened. **FLOWERS** in early summer; male and female on different trees; both small, yellow-green; males in dense short-stalked clusters, females single or in small groups in leaf axils. **FRUIT** in fall or early winter; almost round, about 1/2" long, green turning white, velvety. **FOUND** throughout the Bahamas, in mixed broadleaf areas, sometimes near the shore. Florida. Euphorbiaceae.

COCOPLUM   CHRYSOBALANUS ICACO

10 - 15 feet, often a shrub. **TRUNK** medium short, sometimes leaning. **CROWN** very dense, spreading; branches numerous, erect. **BARK** dark brown, thin, smooth when young; rough, flaking into long pieces with age; pink-red when cut. **TWIGS** red brown to dark brown, straight or slightly zig-zag, medium thick, slightly roughened by numerous lenticels. **LEAVES** evergreen, smooth, firm, dark green and shiny above, slightly paler below, net venation prominent; 1 1/2 - 3" long; stem very short; tip rounded, sometimes blunt pointed or notched; base rounded or wedge. **FLOWERS** in spring, sometimes off and on all year; small, numerous, pale green, on short stalked terminal clusters. **FRUIT** in summer, or off and on all year; white, pink, or black, nearly round, 1 1/2" across; a thin, rather cotton-like flesh considered sweet and edible. **FOUND** throughout the Bahamas, mainly in sandy or swampy areas; common. Florida, West Indies, Mexico, South America. Rosaceae.

MILK BERRY   BUMELIA AMERICANA

10 - 20 feet. **TRUNK** medium to thick, short. **CROWN** spreading, rounded, dense; branches horizontal. **BARK** gray-brown, smooth when young, rough furrows with age. **TWIGS** gray, often mottled, straight or a bit curved, smooth but for numerous leaf scars. **LEAVES** smooth, firm, dark green and shiny above, slightly paler or more often rusty brown below; venation pinnate; 3/4 - 2" long; stem 1/4" long or less; tip rounded or notched, base narrow or wedge, margins often recurved. **FLOWERS** off and on all year, mainly winter and spring; small, pale green, numerous, fragrant, on short axillary stalks. **FRUIT** off and on all year, mainly in summer; about 1/3" long, almost round, black, smooth, shiny; edible though slightly gummy. **FOUND** throughout the Bahamas, generally in coastal areas, sometimes inland in mixed broadleaf areas; fairly common. The alternate leaves may appear to be opposite. Sapotaceae.

ALTERNATE LEAVES   CLUSTERED AT TIP OF TWIG

1. Milky (often irritating) sap
  2. Branches thick, leaf stemmed, round tipped....................................Frangipanni
  2. Branches slender, leaf stemless, sharp tip ....Milk Tree
1. Watery sap
  2. Leaves on thick spur; large tree ....Inagua Oak
  2. Leaves not on thick spur; small tree or shrub...................................Bay Cedar

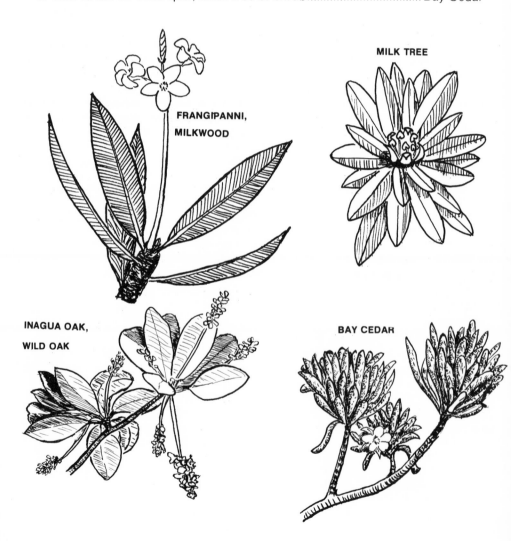

FRANGIPANNI, MILKWOOD

MILK TREE

INAGUA OAK, WILD OAK

BAY CEDAR

FRANGIPANNI   PLUMERIA OBTUSA

8 - 15 feet. **TRUNK** medium thick, short, often leaning; sap white, milky. **CROWN** spreading, open, many erect branches. **BARK** gray to brown, thin, smooth. **TWIGS** gray to brown, thick, straight, smooth, with large leaf scars. **LEAVES** clustered at twig ends; smooth, dark green and shiny above, paler below; innate venation prominent; 4 - 7" long; stem 1 - 1 1/2" long, thick; tip blunt or long or short pointed, base rounded or wedge; sap milky. **FLOWERS** in summer and fall; 1 1/2" across, white with yellow centre, fragrant; in clusters at end of twig. **FRUIT** in fall and winter; brown cylindrical pod 3 - 4" long. **FOUND** throughout the Bahamas, in mixed broadleaf areas, most common along the coasts. Can be propagated by planting a branch. A red variety is found on South Andros. Jamaica, Cuba, Hispaniola. Apocynaceae.

MILK TREE   EUPHORBIA GYMNONOTA

8 - 12 feet. **TRUNK** medium, short; sap milky. **CROWN** spreading and sparse; branches slender. **BARK** gray-green to brown, thin and smooth, rougher with age. **TWIGS** gray to brown, slender, smooth. **LEAVES** often in whorls; medium firm, smooth, bright green and shiny above, paler below; venation indistinct; 1 - 3" long; stem short; tip rounded or short pointed, base narrow wedge. **FLOWERS** off and on all year; showy, bright red bracts, in short-stalked clusters at twig ends. **FRUIT** all year; light green or tinged with red, 1/3" long, rounded, 3 angled, pointed at the top. **FOUND** on San Salvador and the Southern Bahamas, in scrublands. Euphorbiaceae.

INAGUA OAK   BUCIDA BUCERAS

15 - 30 feet. **TRUNK** medium to thick. **CROWN** spreading, symmetrical; branches thick, horizontal. **BARK** gray to brown, thick, rough, furrowed. **TWIGS** gray to brown, zig-zag, medium thick, rough. **LEAVES** in dense whorls; medium firm, smooth, dark green above, paler below; prominent midrib, pinnate venation; 1 1/2 - 3" long; stem 1/4" long; tip blunt, rounded, or notched; base wedge or narrow; margins sometimes recurved. **FLOWERS** in summer and early fall; green-white, very small, fuzzy, numerous; on stalks 1 - 3" long on twig ends. **FRUIT** in summer and winter; 1/4" long, almost conical, brown, dry. **FOUND** on Andros and Inagua, in low areas. West Indies, Panama. Combretaceae.

BAY CEDAR   SURIANA MARITIMA

8 - 12 feet, or shrubby. **TRUNK** short, often twisted. **CROWN** irregular; branches erect. **BARK** dark brown, thick, cracking into strips. **TWIGS** green to brown or red-brown, slender, downy when young, rougher with age. **LEAVES** evergreen, clustered at twig ends; fleshy, smooth, downy, yellow-green and dull, venation indistinct; 1/2 - 1 1/2" long; tip short pointed or rounded, base narrow. **FLOWERS** in spring, rarely through the year; 1/2" long, yellow, in small short-stalked clusters at twig ends. **FRUIT** in summer; pale brown, 1/8" long, dry, with 2 to 5 sections. **FOUND** throughout the Bahamas, along the shore. Bermuda, Florida, shores of the Caribbean. Simaroubaceae.

OPPOSITE LEAVES   SPINY TWIGS

1. Many spines; leaf 1/4 - 1" long, tip round..Wild Guava
1. Few spines
   2. Leaf 1 - 2 1/2" long, not clustered; net veins.......................................Duranta
   2. Leaf 1/2 - 1 1/2" long, clustered; pinnate veins................................ Steelwood

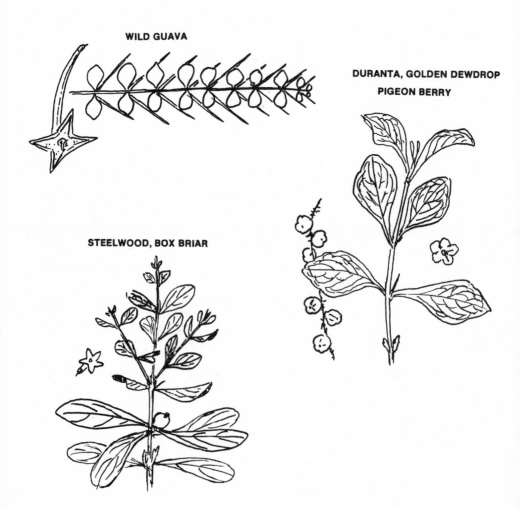

WILD GUAVA

DURANTA, GOLDEN DEWDROP
PIGEON BERRY

STEELWOOD, BOX BRIAR

WILD GUAVA   CATESBAEA SPINOSA

8-10 feet, more often a shrub. **TRUNK** slender, very short. **CROWN** spreading, sparse; branches horizontal, erect or arching, heavily armed with stiff spines 1/2 - 1" long; **BARK** gray-brown, thin, rough, furrowed. **TWIGS** green to gray-brown, slender, straight, with numerous opposite stiff spines about 1/2" long in the axils. **LEAVES** evergreen, smooth, thin, dark green and shiny above, paler below; venation not conspicuous; 1/2 - 1" long, usually shorter than the spines; stem short; tip and base diamond shape (rhombic) or rounded. **FLOWERS** in early summer, occasionally in fall; 4 - 6" long, very showy, light yellow, pendent, single or two in the axils, usually toward the twig ends. **FRUIT** in summer or fall, occasionally in winter; about 1" across, round, yellow, smooth. **FOUND** on Andros, in mixed broadleaf areas. Cuba. Rubiaceae.

DURANTA   DURANTA REPENS

8 - 15 feet, often a shrub. **TRUNK** slender, short. **CROWN** irregular, spreading; branches erect or arching. **BARK** light gray-brown, thin, smooth. **TWIGS** green to brown, slender, straight, more or less smooth, unarmed or spiny. **LEAVES** smooth, thin, bright green to dark green and somewhat shiny above, paler below; net venation; 1 - 2 1/2" long; stem 1/2" long or less; tip blunt or short pointed, base wedge. **FLOWERS** off and on all year; about 1/3" across, pale blue to blue purple, numerous, showy, on terminal or axillary stalks 2 - 4" long. **FRUIT** off and on all year; about 1/3" across, round, orange, smooth, shiny, numerous. **FOUND** throughout the Bahamas, but not on Inagua; very common in mixed broadleaf areas and pine forest. A white flowered race (var. ellisii) is very rare. Bermuda, Florida, West Indies, Mexico, South America. Verbenaceae.

STEELWOOD   RANDIA ACULEATA

10 - 25 feet, often a shrub. **TRUNK** slender, short. **CROWN** narrow, regular, sparse; denser on older trees; branches slender, erect. **BARK** dark brown, thin, smooth, becoming thick, rough and furrowed with age. **TWIGS** brown, slender, straight, slightly roughened by horizontal lines and leaf scars; sometimes armed with a slender, straight spine or two, about 1/3" long, in the axils. **LEAVES** usually in small clusters; smooth, firm, bright green and shiny above, slightly paler below; venation pinnate; 1/2 - 1 1/2" long; stem very short; tip rounded, blunt, or notched, base wedge. **FLOWERS** in summer, occasionally all year; about 1/4" across, white, single or two in the axils on stalks 1/4" long or less. **FRUIT** in fall and winter, occasionally all year; about 1/3" long, more or less round, white, smooth, shiny, with a little crown on top. **FOUND** throughout the Bahamas, in all areas, very common. Bermuda, Florida, West Indies, Mexico. Rubiaceae.

OPPOSITE LEAVES   IRREGULAR MARGINS

1. Leaf margin scalloped
   2. Scallops large; 4 - 8 on leaf 1 - 3" long .... Olive Wood
   2. Scallops small; leaf 1/2 - 1 1/2" long
      3. Leaf bright green, blunt pointed .... Wild Cherry
      3. Leaf bright to dark green, tip rounded .... False Boxwood
1. Leaf margin toothed
   2. Teeth spiny, 5 - 9, leaf stiff .... Seersucker

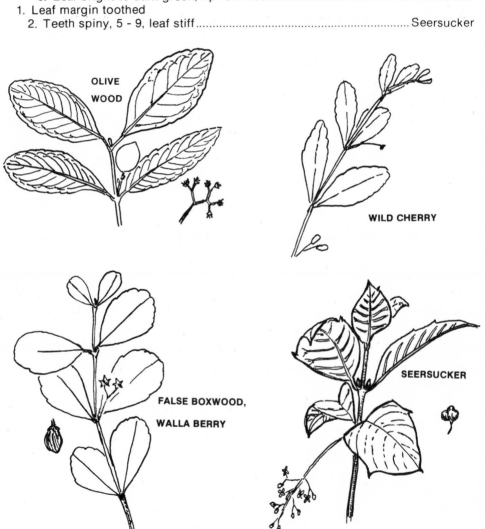

OLIVE WOOD

WILD CHERRY

FALSE BOXWOOD, WALLA BERRY

SEERSUCKER

OLIVE WOOD
CASSINE XYLOCARPA

10 - 25 feet. **TRUNK** medium to thick, short. **CROWN** spreading, medium dense; branches medium, erect. **BARK** gray-brown, generally blotched, smooth, thick. **TWIGS** green to brown, thick, straight, slightly rough. **LEAVES** evergreen, alternate or opposite, smooth, firm, yellow-green to dark green and shiny above, paler below; fine net venation; 1 - 3" long; stem thick, 1/4" long or less; tip rounded or blunt, base wedge. margins strongly recurved. **FLOWERS** in winter, or off and on all year; less than 1/4" across, green, single or several in the axils on very short stalks. **FRUIT** in summer, or all year; globose, about 1/2" across, yellow; a single hard seed. **FOUND** on Abaco, San Salvador, Crooked and Fortune Islands, and Inagua; in coastal and mixed broadleaf areas. Cuba. Celastraceae.

WILD CHERRY
CROSSOPETALUM RHACOMA

8 - 15 feet. **TRUNK** slender, short. **CROWN** irregular, sparse; branches erect, crooked. **BARK** thin, brown, somewhat rough in furrows with age. **TWIGS** green to brown, slender, straight or curved, slightly roughened by faint horizontal lines. **LEAVES** evergreen, smooth, firm, bright green and shiny above, paler below; venation not prominent; 1/2 - 2" long, about 1/3" wide; stem very short; tip short pointed, blunt, or rounded; base wedge or unequal; margins often faintly and bluntly serrate. **FLOWERS** in spring and summer, occasionally all year; 1/8" across or less, green turning red, single or in small clusters on very slender short stalks, axillary or terminal. **FRUIT** in summer and fall, occasionally all year; about 1/4" or less, round, bright red, smooth, shiny. **FOUND** throughout the Bahamas, in mixed broadleaf areas. Bermuda, Florida, West Indies. Celastraceae.

FALSE BOXWOOD
GYMINDA LATIFOLIA

10 - 25 feet. **TRUNK** slender, straight. **CROWN** narrow, medium dense; branches horizontal or drooping, short. **BARK** dark brown, thin, rough in furrows. **TWIGS** gray to brown, slender, straight to crooked, slightly rough. **LEAVES** evergreen, smooth, firm, bright green to dark green and shiny above, paler and shiny below; net venation; 3/4 - 1 1/2" long; stem very short; tip rounded or blunt pointed, sometimes faintly notched; base wedge or unequal; margins faintly and bluntly serrate, sometimes smooth, occasionally recurved. **FLOWERS** in summer, occasionally in winter; male and female flowers on different trees; less than 1/8" across, 1 to 3 on very slender axillary stalk about 1/2" long; **FRUIT** in summer and fall, occasionally in spring; about 1/4" long, oblong, green turning brown, smooth. **FOUND** throughout the Bahamas, but apparently not on New Providence; in mixed broadleaf areas. Florida, Jamaica, Cuba to St. Vincent, Mexico. Celastraceae.

SEERSUCKER
PSEUDOCARPIDIUM WRIGHTII

10 - 15 feet, often a shrub. **TRUNK** slender, short. **CROWN** open, narrow, sparse; branches slender, erect to horizontal. **BARK** gray, often blotched, smooth, thin. **TWIGS** gray to gray-brown, slender, straight, smooth except for lenticels and leaf scars. **LEAVES** very stiff, smooth, bright to dark green and shiny above, paler below; venation pinnate; 1 - 2 1/2" long; stem very short; tip short pointed, base wedge or rounded; margins wavy with several sharp spines about 1/16" long. **FLOWERS** in early summer, occasionally in fall; blue, about 1/4" across, showy, on terminal stalks 2" long. **FRUIT** in late summer and fall, occasionally winter; about 1/3" across, 3- 4 lobed, brown, dry. **FOUND** on Andros, in mixed broadleaf areas, not common. Cuba. Verbenaceae.

OPPOSITE LEAVES HAIRY SURFACE

    2. Teeth soft, not spiny
        3. Leaf irregular, 1/2 - 1 1/4" long, tip rounded...........................Touch-Me-Not
        3. Leaf regular, 1 - 2 1/2" long, tip blunt ....Duranta
1. Leaf with tip rounded
    2. Leaf margin irregular, turned; hair stinging...............................Touch-Me-Not
    2. Leaf margin smooth, hair not stinging
        3. Leaf widest near tip, 1 - 2 1/2" long..Neobracea
        3. Leaf widest near base, 2 - 5" long...Old Man

TOUCH-ME-NOT

DURANTA,
GOLDEN DEWDROP,
PIGEON BERRY

NEOBRACEA

OLD MAN, FROGWOOD

TOUCH-ME-NOT   MALPIGHIA POLYTRICHA

10 - 15 feet, more often a shrub. **TRUNK** short. **CROWN** rather narrow and dense; branches erect. **BARK** gray-brown, thick, smooth; rough with irregular cracks with age. **TWIGS** brown, slender, straight or slightly curved, slightly roughened by lenticels. **LEAVES** evergreen, smooth, firm, bright to dark green and shiny above, paler and sometimes with short stinging hairs below; faintly prominent pinnate venation; 3/4 - 1 1/2" long; stem about 1/8" long; tip rounded, notched, or unequal; base wedge or unequal; margins smooth, bluntly serrate or dentate, sometimes recurved. **FLOWERS** off and on all year; about 1/2" across, pink, five petalled, rather showy, single or in small clusters on axillary or terminal stalks 1/2 - 1" long. **FRUIT** off and on all year; about 1/3" across, bright red, shiny, smooth, round or almost so. **FOUND** throughout the Bahamas, common in all areas. A variable species; small specimens have the stinging hairs; trees in sunlight have bright green leaves, those in shade, dark green. Malpighiaceae.

DURANTA   DURANTA REPENS

8 - 15 feet, often a shrub. **TRUNK** slender, short. **CROWN** irregular, spreading; branches erect or arching. **BARK** light gray-brown, thin, smooth. **TWIGS** green to brown, slender, straight, more or less smooth, unarmed or spiny. **LEAVES** smooth, thin, bright green to dark green and somewhat shiny above, paler below; net venation; 1 - 2 1/2" long; stem 1/2" long or less; tip blunt or short pointed, base wedge. **FLOWERS** off and on all year; about 1/3" across, pale blue to blue purple, numerous, showy, on terminal or axillary stalks 2 - 4" long. **FRUIT** off and on all year; about 1/3" across, round, orange, smooth, shiny, numerous. **FOUND** throughout the Bahamas, but not on Inagua; very common in mixed broadleaf areas and pine forest. A white flowered race (var. ellisii) is very rare. Bermuda, Florida, West Indies, Mexico, South America. Verbenaceae.

NEOBRACEA   NEOBRACEA BAHAMENSIS

8 - 12 feet, more often a shrub. **TRUNK** slender, short. **CROWN** narrow, sparse; branches erect. **BARK** red-brown, smooth, thin. **TWIGS** gray-brown to brown, downy when young, straight, slender, smooth except for leaf scars. **LEAVES** firm, slightly rough, yellow-green and somewhat shiny above, paler below and downy; net venation prominent above, midrib prominent below; 1 - 2 1/2" long; stem about 1/4" or less; tip rounded or slightly notched, base wedge or narrowed; margins often recurved. **FLOWERS** in spring and early summer; about 1" long, tubular, showy, cream-coloured with a dark red throat; somewhat downy inside; singly or few in the axils, on stalks 1" long or less. **FRUIT** in summer; very slender cylindrical pod, 6" long or less, green turning brown. **FOUND** in Northern and Central Bahamas. Apocynaceae.

OLD MAN   GUETTARDA KRUGII

10 - 15 feet. **TRUNK** slender to medium, straight. **CROWN** narrow, open, sparse; branches slender, short, erect, often symmetrical. **BARK** gray, thin, smooth, occasionally blotched. **TWIGS** gray to brown, slender, straight, smooth. **LEAVES** firm, somewhat rough, dark yellow-green and shiny above, downy and pale below; prominent midrib, pinnate venation; 2 - 5" long; stem thick, about 1" long or less; tip rounded or short pointed, base rounded or cordate. **FLOWERS** in summer and fall; tubular, about 1/3" long and wide; white, fragrant, single or in small short-stalked axillary clusters. **FRUIT** in fall and winter; about 1/2" across, globose, pale green or yellow-green, downy, with large seed. **FOUND** throughout the Bahamas, in mixed broadleaf areas, but apparently not on Grand Bahama nor Andros. Puerto Rico. Rubiaceae.

OPPOSITE LEAVES   HAIRY SURFACE

1. Leaf with sharp pointed tip
    2. Leaf rough, dark, veins depressed..............................Rough-Leaf Velvet Seed
    2. Leaf smooth
        3. Leaf 1 - 2″ long, medium shiny..............................Smooth-Leaf Velvet Seed
        3. Leaf 2 - 6″ long, dull..Hairy Wild Coffee

SMOOTH LEAF VELVET SEED   **ROUGH-LEAF VELVET SEED**

HAIRY WILD COFFEE

SMOOTH-LEAF VELVET SEED   GUETTARDA ELLIPTICA

10 - 25 feet. **TRUNK** slender to medium, straight. **CROWN** regular, sparse: branches slender, erect. **BARK** gray to brown, sometimes mottled, smooth, thin. **TWIGS** gray to brown, straight, slender, smooth, with numerous lenticels. **LEAVES** smooth, medium firm, bright to dark green and somewhat shiny above, paler and slightly downy below; prominent midrib and pinnate venation; 1 - 2" long; stem very short; tip short pointed or blunt, base wedge. **FLOWERS** in summer; about 1/3" long, tubular, cream-coloured faintly fragrant, in small clusters on axillary stalks about 1" long. **FRUIT** in fall and early winter; about 1/3" across, downy, very dark red, round, topped by a small crown **FOUND** throughout the Bahamas, common in mixed broadleaf areas. Florida. Jamaica Cuba to Virgin Islands. Rubiaceae.

ROUGH-LEAF VELVET SEED   GUETTARDA SCABRA

10 -25 feet. **TRUNK** slender to medium, straight. **CROWN** narrow and open: branches slender, short, erect, often symmetrical. **BARK** gray-brown, smooth, thin, sometimes flaking with age. **TWIGS** brown, slender, straight, smooth. **LEAVES** firm, rough, dark green and shiny above, much paler and downy below; prominent midrib, pinnate venation; 1 - 5" long; stem about 1/2" long; tip rounded or short pointed, base rounded wedge, or unequal. **FLOWERS** in summer; about 1/2" long, tubular, white, very fragrant in small clusters on axillary stalks 1 - 4" long. **FRUIT** in fall and early winter; about 1/3" across, globose, red, downy, a small crown at the top. **FOUND** throughout the Bahamas; very common in mixed broadleaf areas, sometimes in pine forest. Florida Jamaica, Cuba to Martinique, South America. Rubiaceae.

HAIRY WILD COFFEE   PSYCHOTRIA PUBESCENS

10 feet; usually a shrub. **TRUNK** slender, straight. **CROWN** generally rather spreading, medium dense; branches erect. **BARK** gray, thin, smooth. **TWIGS** green to gray, slender, smooth, straight or curved. **LEAVES** evergreen, somewhat hairy above and below, not firm, very dark green and dull above, much paler below; midrib and pinnate venation prominent on under side; 2 - 6" long; stem rather thick, 1" long or more: tip unequally short or long pointed, base narrowed or wedge, margins sometimes slightly wavy. **FLOWERS** in summer, occasionally all year; less than 1/4" across, cream coloured, numerous on branched terminal spikes 1 - 2" long. **FRUIT** in summer and fall black, smooth, shiny, 1/4" across or less, round. **FOUND** in Northern and Central Bahamas, as an understory tree in mixed broadleaf areas or as a survivor of timber cutting in clearings. Jamaica, Cuba to Virgin Islands. Rubiaceae.

OPPOSITE LEAVES   WIDE TIP

1. Leaf 3 - 6" long
    2. Leaf thick, flat, veins obscure..Wild Mamee
    2. Leaf thin, curled, veins distinct ....Seven Year Apple
1. Leaf smaller, less than 4" long
    2. Leaf tip pointed
        3. Leaf base a long, narrow wedge
            4. Leaf flat, stiff... Guana Berry
            4. Leaf folded, margins high ....Boar Mastic

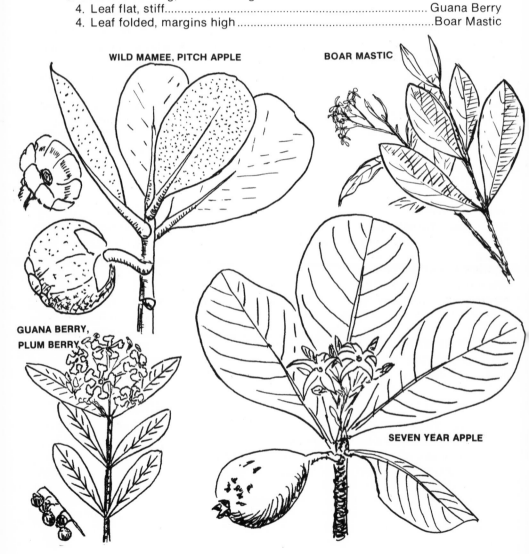

WILD MAMEE, PITCH APPLE

BOAR MASTIC

GUANA BERRY, PLUM BERRY

SEVEN YEAR APPLE

WILD   MAMEE   CLUSIA ROSEA

20 - 50 feet. **TRUNK** medium to thick, short to tall; rarely multiple; aerial roots some-times found near the base. **CROWN** very spreading and dense; branches long, straight, horizontal. **BARK** gray, sometimes blotched, smooth, thin. **TWIGS** brown to gray, thick, straight, somewhat roughened by old leaf scars. **LEAVES** usually in clusters; very leathery, thick; dark green, shiny, smooth above, paler and dull below; venation not prominent; 3 - 6" long and 3 - 5" broad; stem very thick, 1" long or less; tip rounded or slightly notched, base rounded or wedge. **FLOWERS** in mid-winter, occasionally in mid-summer; 3 - 4" across, very showy, white with pink blush on inside of petal; centre yellow-brown, sticky, button-like; flower lasts only a day. **FRUIT** in spring and early summer, occasionally in fall; more or less round, 3 - 4" long, green with brown tip, opening to reveal several seeds in red flesh. **FOUND** in Northern and Central Bahamas, but not on Cat Island, Exuma, nor San Salvador; one of our largest trees, in mixed broadleaf areas. Cuba, tropical America. Guttiferae.

SEVEN YEAR APPLE   CASASIA CLUSIIFOLIA

8 - 15 feet, sometimes a shrub. **TRUNK** slender, short. **CROWN** generally spreading, dense, regular; branches erect. **BARK** brown, thin, smooth. **TWIGS** gray to brown, thick, roughened by old leaf scars. **LEAVES** leathery, smooth, bright to dark green and shiny above, paler below; midrib and net venation prominent; 3 - 6" long; stem very thick, about 1/4" long; tip rounded or blunt, base wedge, margins usually recurved. **FLOWERS** in early summer, showy, 4 - 9 petals, about 1 1/2" across, cream-white, very fragrant, in small clusters at or near twig ends, on stalk 2" long or more. **FRUIT** in winter and spring; green with a reddish cast and small black spots, oval, 2 - 3" long, inedible. **FOUND** throughout the Bahamas, very common in coastal areas. Florida, Bermuda, Cuba. Rubiaceae.

GUANA BERRY   BYRSONIMA LUCIDA

10 - 20 feet. **TRUNK** medium, short, sometimes leaning. **CROWN** spreading, dense; branches horizontal, numerous. **BARK** light to dark brown, occasionally mottled, thin, smooth, slightly rough with age. **TWIGS** gray to brown, slender, short, slightly rough. **LEAVES** evergreen, firm, smooth, dark green and shiny above, much paler and gray-green below; prominent midrib, net venation; 3/4 - 2 1/2" long; tip rounded or sharp pointed, base gradually narrowed; leaf usually erect; **FLOWERS** in spring and early summer, occasionally all year; about 1/2" across, five petalled, white turning pink to dark red, showy, in small clusters at twig ends on branched spike 2 - 4" long. **FRUIT** in summer and fall, occasionally all year; about 1/2" across, round, smooth, green turn-ing red-brown, sour tasting. **FOUND** throughout the Bahamas, mainly in coastal areas, sometimes inland or in scrublands. Florida, Cuba to Barbadoes. Malpighiaceae.

BOAR   MASTIC   LINOCIERA BUMELIOIDES

20 - 30 feet. **TRUNK** medium to thick, often knurled. **CROWN** moderately spreading, dense; branches erect, contorted. **BARK** dark, cracked, very rough. **TWIGS** light gray, slender, hairless, straight, with warty deposits. **LEAVES** medium firm, smooth, dark green and shiny above, paler and conspicuously net veined below; 2 - 4" long; stem thin, 1/2 - 3/4" long; tip rounded or blunt pointed, base wedge; margins smooth, slightly revolute. **FLOWERS** generally in fall, sometimes spring and summer; about 1/3" across and less than 1/3" long, white, not fully opening, few to numerous on axillary and terminal branched stalks. **FRUIT** in spring, sometimes in winter; about 1/4" long, oblong, widest near the base, smooth, black, two seeded, hard under thin layer of flesh. **FOUND** on South Andros only, in mixed broadleaf areas. Cuba. Oleaceae.

OPPOSITE LEAVES   WIDE TIP

    3. Leaf base a blunt wedge, twig ringed ....False Resin Leaf
  2. Leaf tip rounded or notched
    3. Leaf margin recurved
      4. Leaf with pinnate venation...Milk Berry
      4. Leaf with inconspicuous veins
        5. Young twigs with small, scurfy scales.........................Coppice Joewood
        5. Young twigs lacking scales ....Joewood

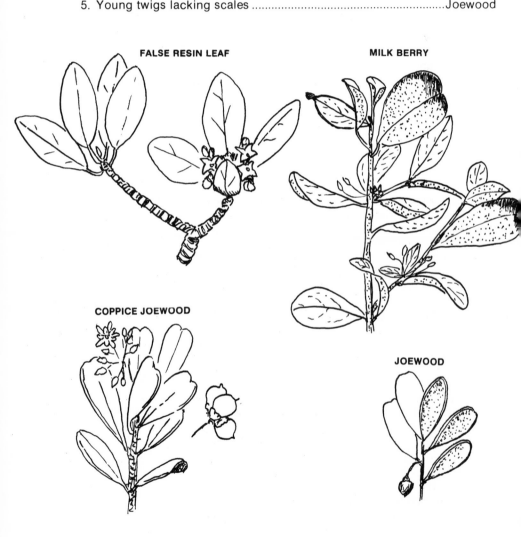

FALSE RESIN LEAF   MILK BERRY

COPPICE JOEWOOD

JOEWOOD

FALSE RESIN LEAF   PHIALLANTHUS MYRTILLOIDES

10 - 15 feet, occasionally a shrub. **TRUNK** slender, straight. **CROWN** narrow, sparse or medium dense; branches slender, erect. **BARK** light gray, sometimes blotched, thin, smooth. **TWIGS** green to light gray, slender, straight, smooth except for leaf scars. **LEAVES** smooth, firm, dark green and shiny above, paler below; venation indistinct, midrib fairly prominent; 3/4 - 2" long; stem very short; tip blunt pointed, base wedge; young leaves appear resinous. **FLOWERS** in winter; about 1/8" across or less, yellow-green, single or very few in short-stalked clusters. **FRUIT** in spring; less than 1/4" across, black, smooth. **FOUND** throughout the Bahamas, in mixed broadleaf areas. Cuba. Rubiaceae.

MILK BERRY   BUMELIA AMERICANA

10 - 20 feet. **TRUNK** medium to thick, short. **CROWN** spreading, rounded, dense; branches horizontal. **BARK** gray-brown, smooth when young, rough furrows with age. **TWIGS** gray, often mottled, straight or a bit curved, smooth but for numerous leaf scars. **LEAVES** smooth, firm, dark green and shiny above, slightly paler or more often rusty brown below; venation pinnate; 3/4 - 2" long; stem 1/4" long or less; tip rounded or notched, base narrow or wedge, margins often recurved. **FLOWERS** off and on all year, mainly winter and spring; small, pale green, numerous, fragrant, on short axillary stalks. **FRUIT** off and on all year, mainly in summer; about 1/3" long, almost round, black, smooth, shiny; edible though slightly gummy. **FOUND** throughout the Bahamas, generally in coastal areas, sometimes inland in mixed broadleaf areas; fairly common. The alternate leaves may appear to be opposite. Sapotaceae.

COPPICE JOEWOOD   JACQUINIA BERTERII

10 - 15 feet, usually a shrub. **TRUNK** slender, short, crooked. **CROWN** spreading, medium dense; branches slender, erect to horizontal. **BARK** gray to dark gray, smooth, thin. **TWIGS** light brown to gray brown, often mottled, generally crooked but sometimes straight, slender, stiff, smooth. **LEAVES** very firm, smooth, bright to dark green on both sides, somewhat shiny above; venation inconspicuous; 3/4 - 1 1/2" long; stem 1/4" long or less; tip rounded, sometimes notched, base narrow or wedge; margins slightly recurved. **FLOWERS** in mid-summer; 1/4" across or less, pale green, faintly fragrant, single or several in small pendant clusters, axillary or terminal. **FRUIT** quickly following the flowers; about 1/4" across, almost round, orange turning black, smooth. **FOUND** apparently throughout the Bahamas, in mixed broadleaf areas; very similar to Joewood, differing in flower colour, leaf colour, and density of the crown. Cuba to Guadeloupe. Theophrastaceae.

JOEWOOD   JACQUINIA KEYENSIS

10 - 15 feet, often a shrub. **TRUNK** medium to thick, short. **CROWN** spreading, dense; branches medium to thick, erect to horizontal. **BARK** gray, often mottled, smooth, thin. **TWIGS** gray to brown, straight or crooked, thick, stiff, smooth. **LEAVES** very firm and smooth, yellow-green to dark green and shiny above, slightly paler below; venation indistinct; 1 - 3" long; stem about 1/4" long; tip rounded, sometimes notched, base narrow or wedge, margins slightly recurved. **FLOWERS** in summer and fall, occasionally in winter; about 1/3" across, white to pale yellow, showy, fragrant, numerous in branched terminal clusters. **FRUIT** in fall and winter, occasionally in spring; almost 1/2" across, nearly round, orange-red, smooth, numerous. **FOUND** throughout the Bahamas, very common along the coast, sometimes found inland. Florida, Cuba, Jamaica. Theophrastaceae.

OPPOSITE LEAVES　　　　　　　　WIDE TIP

3. Leaf margin not recurved
　4. Leaf with stem conspicuously differentiated ....Blolly
　4. Leaf with little apparent stem
　　5. Leaf with pinnate venation prominent ....Steelwood
　　5. Leaf with obscure venation
　　　6. Twig green, smooth with leaf scars .... Black Torch
　　　6. Twig gray, warty ....Boar Mastic

LONG-LEAF BLOLLY, BLOLLY WOOD　　　　**STEELWOOD, BOXWOOD**

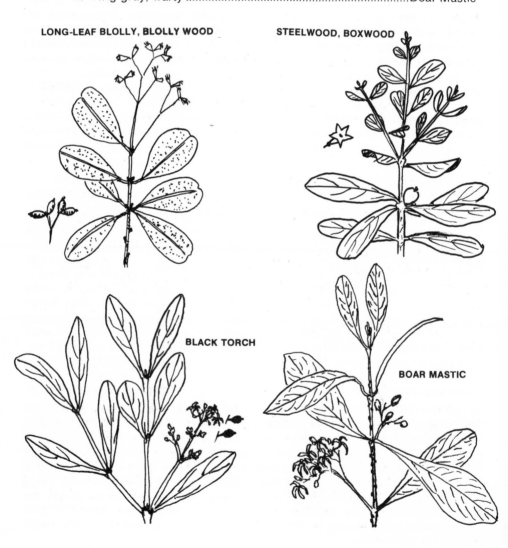

BLACK TORCH

BOAR MASTIC

LONG LEAF BLOLLY

GUAPIRA DISCOLOR

10 - 20 feet. **TRUNK** slender to medium, straight. **CROWN** somewhat spreading, medium dense; branches erect, occasionally drooping. **BARK** gray to brown or red-brown, smooth, thin. **TWIGS** gray to brown, very slender, straight, smooth with occasional leaf scars. **LEAVES** medium firm, smooth, bright yellow-green to green and shiny above, slightly paler below; venation not prominent; 1 - 3" long; stem thin, 1/2" long or more; tip rounded or blunt, base wedge or unequal. **FLOWERS** in summer; small, numerous, yellow-green sometimes tinged with purple; in long-stalked branched terminal clusters. **FRUIT** in late summer and fall; about 1/4" long, ovate, bright red, smooth, shiny. **FOUND** throughout the Bahamas, growing in all areas. When occurring inland, the leaves are thin and narrow, while on the coast they are broader and thicker. Florida, Cuba, Jamaica. Nyctaginaceae.

STEELWOOD

RANDIA ACULEATA

10 - 25 feet, often a shrub. **TRUNK** slender, short. **CROWN** narrow, regular, sparse; denser on older trees; branches slender, erect. **BARK** dark brown, thin, smooth, becoming thick, rough and furrowed with age. **TWIGS** brown, slender, straight, slightly roughened by horizontal lines and leaf scars; sometimes armed with a slender, straight spine or two, about 1/3" long, in the axils. **LEAVES** usually in small clusters; smooth, firm, bright green and shiny above, slightly paler below; venation pinnate; 1/2 - 1 1/2" long; stem very short; tip rounded, blunt, or notched, base wedge. **FLOWERS** in summer, occasionally all year; about 1/4" across, white, single or two in the axils on stalks 1/4" long or less. **FRUIT** in fall and winter, occasionally all year; about 1/3" long, more or less round, white, smooth, shiny, with a little crown on top. **FOUND** throughout the Bahamas, in all areas, very common. Bermuda, Florida, West Indies, Mexico. Rubiaceae.

BLACK TORCH

ERITHALIS FRUTICOSA

10 - 25 feet. **TRUNK** slender to medium, short. **CROWN** spreading, usually regular, medium dense; branches erect, slender, numerous. **BARK** brown, sometimes mottled, thin, smooth. **TWIGS** green to brown, slender, straight, smooth but for leaf scars. **LEAVES** very firm, smooth, dark green and shiny above, paler below; venation not conspicuous; 1 - 3" long; stem rather thick, about 1/4" long; tip short pointed, blunt, or rounded, base wedge. **FLOWERS** in summer, often all year; less than 1/4" across, white, numerous, on axillary stalks about 1 1/2" long. **FRUIT** in summer and fall, often all year; about 1/8" across, purple-black, smooth, shiny, a small crown on top, occasionally almost white when mature. **FOUND** throughout the Bahamas, very common in all areas. A form of this species, lime black torch, has broader, lighter coloured leaves and larger, somewhat fragrant, flowers. Florida, West Indies, Central America. Rubiaceae.

BOAR MASTIC

LINOCIERA BUMELIOIDES

20 - 30 feet. **TRUNK** medium to thick, often knurled. **CROWN** moderately spreading, dense; branches erect, contorted. **BARK** dark, cracked, very rough. **TWIGS** light gray, slender, hairless, straight, with warty deposits. **LEAVES** medium firm, smooth, dark green and shiny above, paler and conspicuously net veined below; 2 - 4" long; stem thin, 1/2 - 3/4" long; tip rounded or blunt pointed, base wedge; margins smooth, slightly revolute. **FLOWERS** generally in fall, sometimes spring and summer; about 1/3" across and less than 1/3" long, white, not fully opening, few to numerous on axillary and terminal branched stalks. **FRUIT** in spring, sometimes in winter; about 1/4" long, oblong, widest near the base, smooth, black, two seeded, hard under thin layer of flesh. **FOUND** on South Andros only, in mixed broadleaf areas. Cuba. Oleaceae.

OPPOSITE LEAVES   WIDE BASE

1. Leaf long pointed
    2. Leaf generally over 2 1/2" long
        3. Leaf markedly 3-ribbed ....Wild Guava
        3. Leaf not 3-ribbed
            4. Leafstem 1/2 - 1 1/2" long
                5. Leaf base rounded, veins raised below....................................Fowl Berry
                5. Leaf base wedge shape, leaf smooth below
                6. Fruit and flowers not stalked.. Fiddlewood
                6. Fruit and flowers stalked... Fiddlewood

WILD GUAVA

FOWL BERRY

FIDDLEWOOD

FIDDLEWOOD

WILD GUAVA   TETRAZYGIA BICOLOR

8 - 15 feet, often a shrub. **TRUNK** slender, short. **CROWN** somewhat spreading, generally regular, medium dense; branches erect. **BARK** gray-brown, thin, rough in furrows.
TWIGS gray-brown, sometimes dark green at the tip, medium thick, short, crooked or
curved, roughened by lenticels and leaf scars. **LEAVES** medium firm, smooth, dark
green and shiny above, silvery and heavily pinnate-veined below, conspicuously three-
nerved on both sides; 2 1/2 - 5" long; tip long pointed, base rounded or unequal.
FLOWERS in spring and summer, occasionally all year; about 3/4" across, four to five
white petals and several bright yellow stamens, very showy, numerous on terminal
stalks 3 - 5" long. **FRUIT** off and on all year, mainly summer and fall; about 1/3" long,
nearly round, black, smooth, dull, a small crown on top. **FOUND** in Northern and
Central Bahamas, but no on San Salvador; mostly in scrub and pinelands, occasionally
in mixed broadleaf forest, but not in heavy shade. Florida, Cuba. Melostomaceae.

FOWL BERRY   PETITIA DOMINGENSIS

10 - 25 feet. **TRUNK** slender to medium, short. **CROWN** very spreading, somewhat
open; branches erect, numerous. **BARK** brown, thin, rough in furrows. **TWIGS** brown,
medium thick, usually curved toward the end, more or less smooth. **LEAVES** firm, bright
green, shiny and somewhat rough above, pale yellow-green and rougher below; midrib
very prominent; pinnate venation; 3 - 6" long; stem about 1 1/2" long, rather thick; tip
short or long pointed, base rounded. **FLOWERS** in spring and summer; less than 1/8"
across, white, numerous, faintly fragrant, on terminal and axillary stalks 3 - 5" long.
FRUIT in summer and fall; about 1/4" across, globose, red turning dark, smooth, shiny.
FOUND in Northern and Central Bahamas, but not on San Salvador; in mixed broadleaf areas, more common in pine forests. Cuba, Jamaica, Puerto Rico. Verbenaceae.

FIDDLEWOOD   CITHAREXYLUM FRUTICOSUM

10 - 20 feet. **TRUNK** slender, straight or crooked. **CROWN** spreading, rather sparse;
branches slender, erect. **BARK** gray-brown, smooth on young trees, becoming rough in
furrows with age. **TWIGS** gray to light brown, straight or slightly curved, slender,
smooth or slightly roughened by horizontal lines. **LEAVES** smooth, medium firm, bright
green and somewhat shiny above, paler and somewhat downy below; prominent midrib, net venation; 2 - 5" long; stem 1" long or less, often pink-brown; tip blunt or short
pointed, base narrow or wedge; margins often wavy. **FLOWERS** in summer and fall;
about 1/4" across, white, fragrant, numerous, nearly stalkless, on terminal spikes 2 - 5"
long. **FRUIT** in fall and winter; about 1/3" across, almost round, orange turning black,
smooth, shiny, numerous, on drooping spikes. **FOUND** throughout the Bahamas, in
mixed broadleaf areas. Florida, Jamaica, Cuba to Guadeloupe. Verbenaceae.

FIDDLEWOOD   CITHAREXYLUM CAUDATUM

10 - 20 feet. **TRUNK** slender, straight to crooked. **CROWN** spreading, rather sparse;
branches slender, erect. **BARK** gray to light brown, smooth on young trees, becoming
rough with age. **TWIGS** gray to light brown, straight or slightly curved, slender, smooth
or slightly roughened by horizontal lines. **LEAVES** medium firm, smooth, bright green
and slightly shiny above, paler and somewhat downy below; prominent midrib and
coarse lateral venation; 2 - 5" long; stem 1" long or less, sometimes pink-brown; tip long
or short pointed or blunt, base narrow or wedge, margins usually wavy. **FLOWERS** in
spring, summer, or fall; about 1/4" across, white, fragrant, numerous, on axillary spikes
2 - 5" long, each individual flower definitely stalked. **FRUIT** in summer, fall, or winter;
1/3" across or less, almost round, orange turning black, smooth, shiny, numerous on
drooping spikes. **FOUND** on Andros only. Cuba to Puerto Rico, Mexico. Verbenaceae.

OPPOSITE LEAVES   WIDE BASE

    4. Leafstem less than 1/2" long
      5. Leaves usually in fours; veins 90° to rib .... Rauwolfia
      5. Leaves in twos; veins more sharply angled
        6. Young leaves resinous .... Resin Leaf
        6. Young leaves not resinous .... Pain-In-Back
  2. Leaf generally under 2 1/2" long
    3. Veins present
      4. Veins 3 - 4 each side; leaf curled .... Princewood

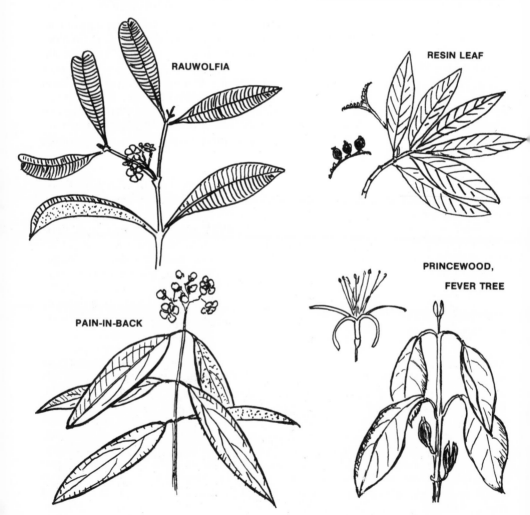

RAUWOLFIA

RESIN LEAF

PAIN-IN-BACK

PRINCEWOOD,
FEVER TREE

RAUWOLFIA
RAUVOLFIA NITIDA

15 - 30 feet. **TRUNK** medium, straight. **CROWN** irregular, medium dense; branches erect. **BARK** gray, thin, smooth. **TWIGS** green to gray, slender, straight, smooth except for scattered lenticels. **LEAVES** firm, smooth, dark green and shiny above, paler below; midrib prominent, pinnate venation; 2 - 6" long; stem 1/2" long or less; tip long pointed, base wedge. **FLOWERS** in spring and summer; 1/3" across, white, showy, numerous in clusters on branched axillary stalks 1/2" long or more. **FRUIT** in summer and fall; about 1/3" across, more or less round, red turning near black, smooth, somewhat milky inside, two-seeded. **FOUND** on New Providence and Abaco, generally in coastal areas; rare. Jamaica, Cuba to Virgin Islands. Apocynaceae.

RESIN LEAF
TEREBRARIA RESINOSA

10 - 20 feet. **TRUNK** slender, straight. **CROWN** regular and symmetrical, medium dense; branches slender, erect. **BARK** gray, thin, smooth, often mottled and flaking on older trees. **TWIGS** green, gray, or light brown, slender, straight, more or less smooth. **LEAVES** smooth, medium firm, dark green and very shiny above, somewhat paler below; venation pinnate; 2 - 4 1/2" long; stem about 1/4" long; tip long pointed, base narrow or wedge; young leaves appear to be resinous. **FLOWERS** in summer and fall; about 1/4" across, white, few, on forked terminal stalks about 2" long. **FRUIT** in fall and winter; about 1/4" across or less, globose, black, shiny, smooth. **FOUND** in Northern and Central Bahamas, in mixed broadleaf areas, more rarely in pineland, nowhere common. Cuba. Rubiaceae.

PAIN-IN-BACK
BUNCHOSIA GLANDULOSA

10 - 20 feet. **TRUNK** slender, short. **CROWN** rather narrow, medium dense; branches erect. **BARK** brown, thin, rough in vertical furrows. **TWIGS** brown, straight, slender, somewhat roughened by numerous lenticels. **LEAVES** smooth, medium firm, dark green and shiny above, paler below; fairly prominent midrib, net venation; 1 1/2 - 3 1/2" long; stem about 1/3" long; tip usually short pointed, base rounded or wedge. **FLOWERS** in early summer; about 1/3" across, bright yellow, five petaled, showy, numerous in small axillary clusters on 1 - 2" stalks. **FRUIT** in summer; round, smooth, about 1/3" across, orange-red, showy. **FOUND** in Central Bahamas and Long Island, in mixed broadleaf areas, but not common. Hispaniola, Puerto Rico to Martinique, Yucatan. Malpighiaceae.

PRINCEWOOD
EXOSTEMA CARIBAEUM

20 - 50 feet. **TRUNK** medium to thick, straight, tall. **CROWN** somewhat spreading, often rounded, medium dense; branches erect, straight. **BARK** gray, mottled, smooth, thin; rough, cracking into small pieces with age. **TWIGS** gray-brown, slender, straight, with numerous lenticels and leaf scars. **LEAVES** smooth, medium firm, dark yellow-green and shiny above, much paler and dull below; midvein fairly prominent; 1 - 2 1/2" long; stem 1/2" long or less; tip short or long pointed, base wedge, margins often wavy. **FLOWERS** in summer; about 1 1/2" across, slender petals white turning light brown within the day; very showy; single or few on short axillary stalks, fragrant. **FRUIT** in winter and spring; about 1/3" long, ovoid, smooth, green turning almost black and drying. **FOUND** throughout the Bahamas in mixed broadleaf areas; quite common. Florida, Cuba to Grenada, Jamaica, Central America. Rubiaceae.

OPPOSITE LEAVES   WIDE BASE

    4. Veins 6 or more each side; margin wavy ....White Stopper
  3. Veins obscure
    4. Leaf very stiff, shiny ....Red Stopper
    4. Leaf flat, medium firm, dull...Ironwood
1. Leaf short pointed, blunt, or rounded
  2. Leaf short pointed or blunt pointed
    3. Leaf short pointed
      4. Leaf shiny, stiff, 1 1/4 - 1 1/2" long...Parrot Wood

WHITE STOPPER

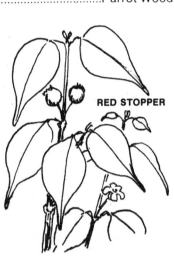

RED STOPPER

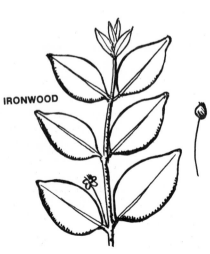

IRONWOOD

PARROT WOOD

WHITE STOPPER
EUGENIA AXILLARIS

10 - 20 feet. **TRUNK** slender, straight. **CROWN** narrow, medium dense; branches short, erect. **BARK** light gray, thin, smooth, splitting into small pieces on old trees. **TWIGS** light gray to light brown, slender, straight or a bit curved, smooth. **LEAVES** evergreen, smooth, firm, dark green and shiny above, paler below; venation indistinct; 1 - 2 1/2" long; stem 1/2" long or less, often red-brown; tip short or long pointed, base wedge or narrow; leaf aromatic when crushed. **FLOWERS** in summer and fall, sometimes early winter; about 1/4" across, white, many short stamens, numerous in short-stalked axillary clusters; slightly fragrant. **FRUIT** in winter and spring, occasionally early summer; 1/3" or more across, almost round, black, smooth, dull; taste spicy, considered edible. **FOUND** throughout the Bahamas, growing in all areas, and occurring in several varieties. Entire plant exudes faint skunk-like odor. Bermuda, Florida, Jamaica, Cuba to Guadeloupe. Myrtaceae.

RED STOPPER
EUGENIA CONFUSUM

15 - 35 feet. **TRUNK** slender to medium, straight. **CROWN** narrow, very dense; branches erect. **BARK** dark brown, thick, rough, flaking into small pieces. **TWIGS** light brown to gray, slender, straight or somewhat curved, smooth. **LEAVES** evergreen, smooth, very firm, dark green and very shiny above, paler and yellow-green below; venation obscure; 1 - 2 1/2" long; stem about 1/3" long; tip very long pointed, base rounded or wedge; leaf aromatic when crushed. **FLOWERS** in summer; 1/4" across or less, white to cream, single or few in small axillary short-stalked clusters. **FRUIT** in summer and fall; about 1/4" across, round or almost so, bright to dark red, shiny, smooth. **FOUND** throughout the Bahamas, but apparently not on Mayaguana nor Inagua; in mixed broadleaf areas, moderately common. Florida, Jamaica, Cuba to Puerto Rico. Myrtaceae.

IRONWOOD
EUGENIA RHOMBEA

8 - 15 feet, sometimes a shrub. **TRUNK** slender to medium, short. **CROWN** narrow, very dense; branches erect, numerous. **BARK** gray-brown, smooth, thin; flaking with age. **TWIGS** gray-brown, sometimes mottled, crooked, medium thick, smooth but for occasional leaf scars. **LEAVES** evergreen, smooth, firm, yellow-green to dark green and dull above, slightly paler below; venation not prominent; 1 - 2" long; stem short, red-brown or yellow; tip short or blunt pointed, base wedge; leaf aromatic when crushed. **FLOWERS** in summer and fall; about 1/4" across, white, with numerous short yellow stamens, in small, short-stalked axillary clusters. **FRUIT** in winter and spring; 1/3 - 1/2" across, nearly globose, dark red to black, dull, smooth; sharp tasting and spicy, but considered edible. **FOUND** in Southern Bahamas, in mixed broadleaf areas and scrublands; not common. Florida, Jamaica, Cuba to Guadeloupe. Myrtaceae.

PARROT WOOD
BUXUS BAHAMENSIS

8 - 15 feet. **TRUNK** slender, short. **CROWN** narrow, medium dense; branches erect, short. **BARK** gray-brown, mottled, thick and rough in vertical furrows. **TWIGS** gray-brown, somewhat mottled, rough with numerous lenticels. **LEAVES** smooth stiff, bright to dark green and shiny above, slightly paler and somewhat shiny below; midrib prominent; 1/2 - 1" long; stem very short; tip short pointed, blunt, or rounded; base narrow wedge; leaf generally held erect. **FLOWERS** off and on all year; very small, yellow-green in small, very short-stalked clusters in leaf axils. **FRUIT** off and on all year; about 1/4" across, more or less round, yellow-green to yellow-orange, with three small horns at the tip. **FOUND** throughout the Bahamas, in mixed broadleaf areas, scrublands, and marshes. Cuba, Jamaica. Buxaceae.

OPPOSITE LEAVES   WIDE BASE

  4. Leaf soft, dull
    5. Leaf base rounded; many veins ....Smooth-Leaf Velvet Seed
    5. Leaf base very narrow; few veins..Duranta
3. Leaf blunt pointed
  4. Tree growing in salt water... Red Mangrove
  4. Tree growing in woodland
    5. Leaves clustered at twig tip; leaf shiny ....Quina

DURANTA,

GOLDEN DEWDROP,

PIGEON BERRY

SMOOTH LEAF VELVET SEED

RED MANGROVE

QUINA

SMOOTH-LEAF VELVET SEED   GUETTARDA ELLIPTICA

10 - 25 feet. **TRUNK** slender to medium, straight, **CROWN** regular, sparse; branches slender, erect. **BARK** gray to brown, sometimes mottled, smooth, thin. **TWIGS** gray to brown, straight, slender, smooth, with numerous lenticels. **LEAVES** smooth, medium firm, bright to dark green and somewhat shiny above, paler and slightly downy below; prominent midrib and pinnate venation; 1 - 2" long; stem very short; tip short pointed or blunt, base wedge. **FLOWERS** in summer; about 1/3" long, tubular, cream-coloured, faintly fragrant, in small clusters on axillary stalks about 1" long. **FRUIT** in fall and early winter; about 1/3" across, downy, very dark red, round, topped by a small crown. **FOUND** throughout the Bahamas, common in mixed broadleaf areas. Florida, Jamaica, Cuba to Virgin Islands. Rubiaceae.

DURANTA   DURANTA REPENS

8 - 15 feet, often a shrub. **TRUNK** slender, short. **CROWN** irregular, spreading; branches erect or arching. **BARK** light gray-brown, thin, smooth. **TWIGS** green to brown, slender, straight, more or less smooth, unarmed or spiny. **LEAVES** smooth, thin, bright green to dark green and somewhat shiny above, paler below; net venation; 1 - 2 1/2" long; stem 1/2" long or less; tip blunt or short pointed, base wedge. **FLOWERS** off and on all year; about 1/3" across, pale blue to blue purple, numerous, showy, on terminal or axillary stalks 2 - 4" long. **FRUIT** off and on all year; about 1/3" across, round, orange, smooth, shiny, numerous. **FOUND** throughout the Bahamas, but not on Inagua; very common in mixed broadleaf areas and pine forest. A white flowered race (var. ellisii) is very rare. Bermuda, Florida, West Indies, Mexico, South America. Verbenaceae.

RED MANGROVE   RHIZOPHORA MANGLE

15 - 40 feet. **TRUNK** medium to thick, short to tall. **CROWN** generally regular and rounded, occasionally tall and narrow; branches wide, spreading, the lower ones often with aerial roots. **BARK** red-brown to brown, thin, smooth, becoming rough with age. **TWIGS** brown, thick, straight, very smooth with occasional or numerous leaf scars. **LEAVES** smooth, thick, very firm, yellow-green to dark green and shiny above, much paler below; midrib thick and prominent, venation obscure; 2 - 6" long; stem very thick, about 1/2" long; tip blunt pointed or rounded, base rounded or wedge **FLOWERS** all year; about 3/4" across, four petalled, yellow, downy, slightly fragrant, in twos and threes on long axillary stalk. **FRUIT** all year, a radicle 8 - 12" when mature, the stem end green, the tip (a developing root) brown. **FOUND** throughout the Bahamas, along the coast and in wet ground. Bermuda, Florida to Brazil, Africa, the Pacific. Rhizophoraceae.

QUINA   ANTIRHEA LUCIDA..

10 - 25 feet. **TRUNK** slender to medium, straight. **CROWN** somewhat spreading, dense; branches erect to horizontal. **BARK** light to dark gray, thin, smooth, roughening and flaking on older trees. **TWIGS** gray, slender, straight, smooth. **LEAVES** often in fours; bright green and shiny above, paler below; venation not prominent; 1 1/2 - 4 1/2" long; stem rather thick, 1/3" long or less; tip short pointed, blunt, or rounded; base narrow or wedge. **FLOWERS** in summer; about 1/4" long, white, fragrant, several on forked terminal stalk. **FRUIT** in late summer and fall; about 1/4" long, oblong, black, smooth, shiny, with a small crown on top. **FOUND** throughout the Bahamas, in mixed broadleaf areas; widespread, but not common. Jamaica, Cuba to Trinidad. Rubiaceae.

OPPOSITE LEAVES   WIDE BASE

  5. Leaves not clustered at twig tip
     6. Leaf nearly stemless; dotted beneath..........................Bahama Stopper
     6. Leaf with distinct stem
       7. Midrib not impressed..Boar Mastic
       7. Midrib impressed, margins slightly curled
         8. New growth faintly downy.. Spicewood
         8. New growth not downy; leaf shiny.....................Myrtle-of-the-River

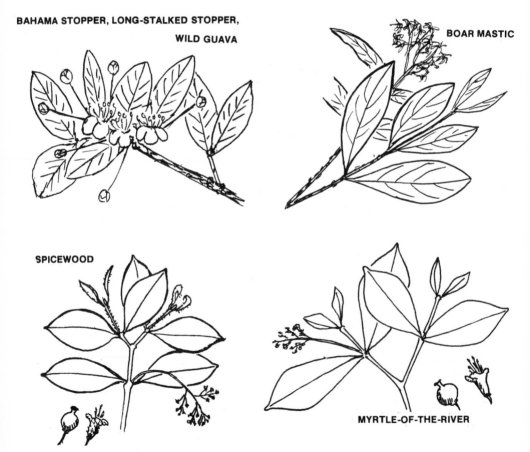

BAHAMA STOPPER, LONG-STALKED STOPPER,

WILD GUAVA

BOAR MASTIC

SPICEWOOD

MYRTLE-OF-THE-RIVER

BAHAMA STOPPER   PSIDIUM LONGIPES

8 - 12 feet, more often a shrub. **TRUNK** short, slender, usually twisted. **CROWN** narrow, sparse, occasionally medium dense; branches few, short, crooked. **BARK** gray to brown, thin, often flaking. **TWIGS** gray to brown, straight or curved, smooth but for a few leaf scars. **LEAVES** evergreen, firm, smooth, yellow-green to dark green and shiny above, paler below; venation obscure; numerous punctate dots visible from below; 3/4 - 1 1/2" long; stem very short, red-brown or yellow; tip short pointed, rounded, or blunt; base wedge, narrow, or rounded; leaf aromatic when crushed. **FLOWERS** in summer and fall; about 1/3" across, white, stamens numerous, somewhat fragrant, solitary or few on axillary stalks 1 1/2" long or less. **FRUIT** in summer and fall; about 1/2" long, almost round, dark red, dull, smooth, with a small crown on top; edible. **FOUND** throughout the Bahamas, in scrubland and mixed broadleaf areas. A variety, var. orbiculare, of Northern and Central Bahamas, has flowers 1/2" across and leaves that are more rounded. Florida. Myrtaceae.

BOAR MASTIC   LINOCIERA BUMELIOIDES

20 - 30 feet. **TRUNK** medium to thick, often knurled. **CROWN** moderately spreading, dense; branches erect, contorted. **BARK** dark, cracked, very rough. **TWIGS** light gray, slender, hairless, straight, with warty deposits. **LEAVES** medium firm, smooth, dark green and shiny above, paler and conspicuously net veined below; 2 - 4" long; stem thin, 1/2 - 3/4" long; tip rounded or blunt pointed, base wedge; margins smooth, slightly revolute. **FLOWERS** generally in fall, sometimes spring and summer; about 1/3" across and less than 1/3" long, white, not fully opening, few to numerous on axillary and terminal branched stalks. **FRUIT** in spring, sometimes in winter; about 1/4" long, oblong, widest near the base, smooth, black, two seeded, hard under thin layer of flesh. **FOUND** on South Andros only, in mixed broadleaf areas. Cuba. Oleaceae.

SPICEWOOD   CALYPTRANTHES PALLENS

10 - 20 feet. **TRUNK** slender to medium, straight. **CROWN** somewhat spreading, medium dense; branches horizontal to erect. **BARK** pale gray, thin, smooth, sometimes peeling; rough in furrows with age. **TWIGS** gray to brown, slender, straight or curved, smooth. **LEAVES** evergreen, smooth, firm, dark green and faintly shiny above, paler below; venation pinnate but obscure; 1 - 2 1/2" long; stem very short; tip long pointed, base wedge; margins usually somewhat wavy; leaf aromatic when crushed; new growth faintly downy. **FLOWERS** in spring and summer; small, petalless, pale brown, many short stamens, numerous on long-stalked, much branched axillary or terminal clusters. **FRUIT** in summer and fall; 1/4" across or less, almost round, black, dull, smooth. **FOUND** throughout the Bahamas, but apparently not on Inagua; in mixed broadleaf areas; not common. Florida, Jamaica, Cuba to Guadeloupe. Myrtaceae.

MYRTLE OF THE RIVER   CALYPTRANTHES ZUZYGIUM

10 - 20 feet. **TRUNK** slender, straight. **CROWN** somewhat spreading, sometimes narrow, medium dense; branches erect. **BARK** light gray, thin, smooth. **TWIGS** gray-brown, slender, straight or zig-zag, smooth, with a small gland immediately above the leaf axil. **LEAVES** evergreen, smooth, firm, dark green and shiny above, paler below; pinnate venation, midrib fairly prominent; 1 - 2 1/2" long; stem very short; tip long pointed, base wedge or unequal; leaf aromatic when crushed. **FLOWERS** in summer or late summer; small, petalless, with many short stamens, creamy white, in axillary or terminal clusters of one to five blossoms, 1/4" across, almost round, black, smooth, dull. **FOUND** on Abaco, New Providence, and Andros, in mixed broadleaf areas; not common. The leaf is shinier than that of the above species. Florida, Jamaica, Cuba, Hispaniola. Myrtaceae.

OPPOSITE LEAVES   WIDE BASE

2. Leaf tip round pointed or notched
  3. Leaf with narrow base
    4. Leaf with visible veins
      5. Leaf stiff, rust-brown below...Milk Berry
      5. Leaf not rust-brown below
        6. Leaf margin turned down; buds dark brown ....Beefwood
        6. Leaf flat, leafbuds green .... Black Torch
    4. Leaf with obscure veins
      5. Leaf surface dotted with white above, dark below
        6. Bark gray-brown, rough; fruit black ....Spanish Stopper

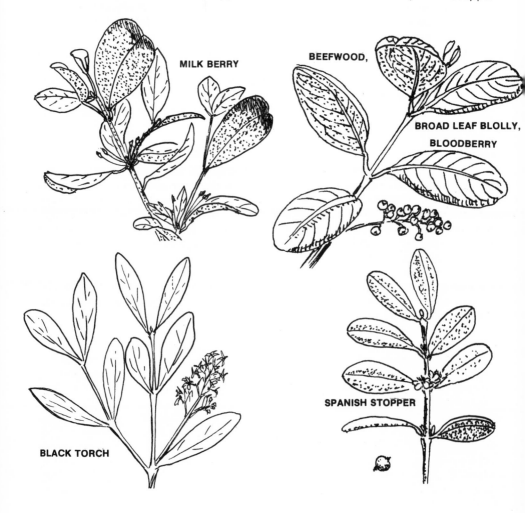

MILK BERRY

BEEFWOOD,

BROAD LEAF BLOLLY,

BLOODBERRY

BLACK TORCH

SPANISH STOPPER

MILK BERRY   BUMELIA AMERICANA

10 - 20 feet. **TRUNK** medium to thick, short. **CROWN** spreading, rounded, dense; branches horizontal. **BARK** gray-brown, smooth when young, rough furrows with age. **TWIGS** gray, often mottled, straight or a bit curved, smooth but for numerous leaf scars. **LEAVES** smooth, firm, dark green and shiny above, slightly paler or more often rusty brown below; venation pinnate; 3/4 - 2" long; stem 1/4" long or less; tip rounded or notched, base narrow or wedge, margins often recurved. **FLOWERS** off and on all year, mainly winter and spring; small, pale green, numerous, fragrant, on short axillary stalks. **FRUIT** off and on all year, mainly in summer; about 1/3" long, almost round, black, smooth, shiny; edible though slightly gummy. **FOUND** throughout the Bahamas, generally in coastal areas, sometimes inland in mixed broadleaf areas; fairly common. The alternate leaves may appear to be opposite. Sapotaceae.

BEEFWOOD   GUAPIRA OBTUSA

20 - 40 feet. **TRUNK** medium, straight, tall. **CROWN** spreading, dense, generally regular; branches thick, erect. **BARK** gray, sometimes gray-brown, slightly rough, slightly furrowed with age. **TWIGS** gray-brown, straight, crooked, or twisted, smooth or slightly rough. **LEAVES** smooth, leathery, very firm, dark to very dark green and shiny above, paler below; stem prominent, venation not outstanding; 2 - 4" long, 1 - 2" broad; stem stout, about 1/4" long; tip rounded or notched, base rounded or wedge, margins slightly recurved. **FLOWERS** in summer; small, numerous, yellow-green, at the end of the twig in long-stalked, much-branched clusters; fragrant. **FRUIT** in summer and fall; about 1/4" long, numerous, showy, bright red, juicy, smooth, shiny. **FOUND** in Northern and Central Bahamas, but apparently not on Andros; generally common. Cuba, Santo Domingo. Nyctaginaceae.

BLACK TORCH   ERITHALIS FRUTICOSA

10 - 25 feet. **TRUNK** slender to medium, short. **CROWN** spreading, usually regular, medium dense; branches erect, slender, numerous. **BARK** brown, sometimes mottled, thin, smooth. **TWIGS** green to brown, slender, straight, smooth but for leaf scars. **LEAVES** very firm, smooth, dark green and shiny above, paler below; venation not conspicuous; 1 - 3" long; stem rather thick, about 1/4" long; tip short pointed, blunt, or rounded, base wedge. **FLOWERS** in summer, often all year; less than 1/4" across, white, numerous, on axillary stalks about 1 1/2" long. **FRUIT** in summer and fall, often all year; about 1/8" across, purple-black, smooth, shiny, a small crown on top, occasionally almost white when mature. **FOUND** throughout the Bahamas, very common in all areas. A form of this species, lime black torch, has broader, lighter coloured leaves and larger, somewhat fragrant, flowers. Florida, West Indies, Central America. Rubiaceae.

SPANISH STOPPER   EUGENIA FOETIDA

15 - 35 feet. **TRUNK** slender, occasionally medium, straight. **CROWN** narrow, medium dense; branches slender, erect. **BARK** light brown to gray, thin, smooth, roughening with age and cracking into small thin pieces. **TWIGS** brown to gray, slender, straight or slightly curved, somewhat roughened by faint lines and leaf scars. **LEAVES** evergreen, smooth, firm, dark green and shiny above, paler below; venation obscure; 3/4 - 2" long; stem short; tip blunt pointed or rounded, base narrow or wedge; leaf aromatic when crushed. **FLOWERS** in summer and fall; about 1/8" across, white, many stamens, somewhat fragrant, numerous in few-flowered, short-stalked axillary clusters. **FRUIT** in fall and winter, sometimes in spring, about 1/8" across, round, dull black, smooth. **FOUND** throughout the Bahamas, growing in all areas, and confusing with its many varieites. Florida, Cuba to Virgin Islands, Jamaica. Myrtaceae.

OPPOSITE LEAVES   WIDE BASE

      6. Bark light gray and pink; fruit red ....Naked Wood
    5. Leaf surface lacking dots
      6. Leaf margin often curled and/or scalloped ....False Boxwood
      6. Leaf flat, margins smooth ....Swamp Bush
  3. Leaf with wide base
    4. Leaf tip rounded, not notched
      5. Coastal tree, sometimes in swamps
        6. Leaf dark green above, gray below ....Black Mangrove

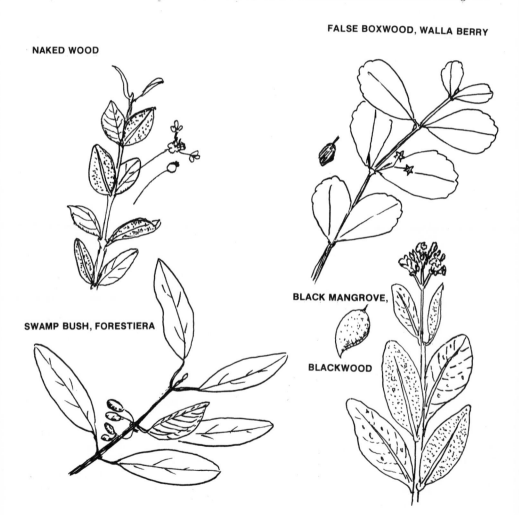

FALSE BOXWOOD, WALLA BERRY

NAKED WOOD

SWAMP BUSH, FORESTIERA

BLACK MANGROVE,

BLACKWOOD

NAKED WOOD   MYRCIANTHES FRAGRANS

15 - 20 feet. **TRUNK** moderately thick, sometimes slender. **CROWN** usually rather narrow, occasionally somewhat spreading; branches erect. **BARK** pale red-brown, hairless, smooth. **LEAVES** leathery, medium green and dull above; veins scarely noticeable, midrib deeply impressed on upper surface and raised on lower suface; 1 - 3″ long; tip blunt pointed, rarely notched; base wedge; margins smooth, slightly revolute; leaf aromatic when crushed. **FLOWERS** early spring through midsummer; about 1/2″ across, petals four or five, white, numerous yellow stamens, three to seven blossoms together. **FRUIT** in late spring through early fall; 3/4″ across, more or less round, red, several seeds. **FOUND** throughout the Bahamas, but apparently not on San Salvador nor New Providence; in mixed broadleaf areas. Cuba. Myrtaceae.

FALSE BOX WOOD   GYMINDA LATIFOLIA

10 - 25 feet. **TRUNK** slender, straight. **CROWN** narrow, medium dense; branches horizontal or drooping, short. **BARK** dark brown, thin, rough in furrows. **TWIGS** gray to brown, slender, straight to crooked, slightly rough. **LEAVES** evergreen, smooth, firm, bright green to dark green and shiny above, paler and shiny below; net venation; 3/4 - 1 1/2″ long; stem very short; tipor blunt pointed, sometimes faintly notched; base wedge or unequal; margins faintly and bluntly serrate, sometimes smooth, occasionally recurved. **FLOWERS** in summer, occasionally in winter; male and female flowers on different trees; less than 1/8″ across, 1 to 3 on very slender axillary stalk about 1/2″ long; **FRUIT** in summer and fall, occasionally in spring; about 1/4″ long, oblong, green turning brown, smooth. **FOUND** throughout the Bahamas, but apparently not on New Providence; in mixed broadleaf areas. Florida, Jamaica, Cuba to St. Vincent, Mexico. Celastraceae.

SWAMP BUSH   FORESTIERA SEGREGATA

8 - 15 feet. **TRUNK** slender, short. **CROWN** generally spreading, medium dense, irregular; branches slender, erect, sometimes crooked. **BARK** light gray to brown, thin, smooth. **TWIGS** light gray to brown, slender, straight, slightly roughened by horizontal lines and lenticels. **LEAVES** firm, smooth, bright to dark green and shiny above, paler and with a very conspicuous net venation below; 3/4 - 2″ long; stem about 1/4″ long, often red-brown; tip rounded or blunt pointed, base wedge. **FLOWERS** off and on all year, mainly in spring and summer; male and female on different trees; male very small, pale yellow, fragrant, in short-stalked clusters in the axils; females larger, also in small clusters. **FRUIT** off and on all year, mainly in fall and winter; about 1/4″ long, smooth, ovate, green to blue-black. **FOUND** throughout the Bahamas, fairly common in mixed broadleaf areas. Bermuda, Florida, Jamaica, Cuba to Virgin Islands. Oleaceae.

BLACK MANGROVE   AVICENNIA GERMINANS

15 - 25 feet. **TRUNK** medium, short. **CROWN** spreading, irregular, medium dense; branches numerous, erect. **BARK** brown to dark gray, smooth on young trees, rough and fissured with age. **TWIGS** gray to brown, thick, smooth, slightly downy when young, enlarged at the joints. **LEAVES** very firm and smooth, yellow-green to dark green and shiny above, gray-green and downy below; venation pinnate; 2 - 4″ long; stem 1/2″ long or less; tip rounded or short pointed, base wedge. **FLOWERS** off and on all year; about 1/3″ across, white, numerous in dense clusters on downy terminal stalks 1 - 2″ long. **FRUIT** off and on all year; about 1″ long, yellow-green, flattened, oblong, slightly downy, often splitting. **FOUND** throughout the Bahamas, very common on the coast and in swamps. Bermuda, Florida to Texas, West Indies, South America. Verbenaceae.

OPPOSITE LEAVES   WIDE BASE

    6. Leaf light green both sides, thick .... White Mangrove
  5. Tree of inland woods
    6. Leaf margin irregular, veins sunken ....Pisonia
    6. Leaf margins smooth
      7. Veins obscure
        8. Leaf dotted (punctate); 1 - 3 leaflets .... Marigold
        8. Leaf rough, not dotted; 1 - 5 leaflets .... Chicken Toe

WHITE MANGROVE

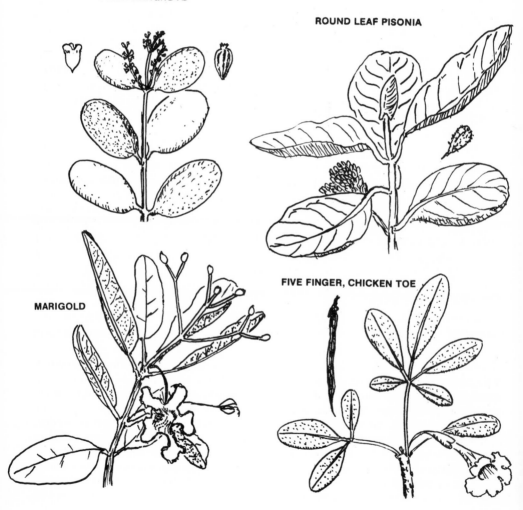

ROUND LEAF PISONIA

MARIGOLD

FIVE FINGER, CHICKEN TOE

WHITE MANGROVE   LAGUNCULARIA RACEMOSA

10 - 25 feet. **TRUNK** medium to thick, sometimes leaning. **CROWN** irregular, often spreading, not dense; branches crooked, numerous. **BARK** dark brown, thick, very rough, furrowed. **TWIGS** green to brown, slender, straight, smooth. **LEAVES** evergreen, firm, smooth, bright green and shiny on both sides; venation obscure, midrib thick; 1 - 2 1/2" long; stem thick, pale red, 1/2" long or less; tip rounded or notched, base rounded; leaf generally held erect. **FLOWERS** off and on all year; very small, numerous, white, on branched axillary and terminal stalks 2 - 4" long. **FRUIT** off and on all year; gray-green, downy, turning brown, about 1/2" long. **FOUND** throughout the Bahamas, very common in coastal and swamp areas. Florida, West Indies, tropical American coasts. Combretaceae.

PISONIA   PISONIA ROTUNDATA

8 - 15 feet, more often a shrub. **TRUNK** slender, short. **CROWN** somewhat spreading, open, sparse, occasionally medium dense; branches erect. **BARK** brown or gray-brown, blotched, smooth, thin. **TWIGS** brown, straight, slender, smooth except for leaf scars. **LEAVES** very firm, slightly rough, dark green and shiny above, paler below; prominent midrib, pinnate venation (especially below); 1 - 2 1/2" long; stem rather thick, 1/2" long or less; tip rounded, base rounded or wedge. **FLOWERS** in spring and early summer; small, numerous, pale green on branched axillary stalks about 2" long. **FRUIT** in summer; about 1/4" long, more or less round, dry. **FOUND** in Northern and Central Bahamas, but apparently not on San Salvador; generally in pine forests or scrubland. Florida, Cuba. Nyctaginaceae.

MARIGOLD   CATALPA PUNCTATA

10 - 30 feet. **TRUNK** slender to medium, straight. **CROWN** regular, medium dense; branches erect. **BARK** gray-brown, thick, rough in vertical furrows. **TWIGS** light brown, straight or crooked, smooth with occasional leaf scars. **LEAVES** generally single, sometimes in threes; smooth, smooth, medium firm, bright green and rather dull above, paler below; midrib prominent, net venation, punctate above and below; 1 - 2 1/2" long; stem about 1" long; tip and base rounded or blunt. **FLOWERS** in early summer; about 1" long; light yellow with deep red centre and two yellow bands in the throat, very frilly, showy, several to each branched terminal stalk. **FRUIT** in summer; 3 - 7" long, slender cylindrical brown pod, sometimes curled at the end. **FOUND** only on South Andros, where it is not uncommon in mixed broadleaf areas. Cuba. Bignoniaceae.

CHICKEN TOE   TABEBUIA BAHAMENSIS

20 - 50 feet. **TRUNK** slender to medium, straight, tall. **CROWN** narrow, sparse; branches short, erect. **BARK** brown to gray, thick, very rough in vertical furrows. **TWIGS** gray-brown, straight or slightly crooked, medium thick, roughened by numerous leaf scars. **LEAVES** with leaflet number variable from one to seven; smooth, firm, dark green and shiny above, pale gray-green below; midrib prominent, net venation; 1 - 3" long; stem 1/4 - 1" long; tip rounded or blunt, often notched, base rounded or wedge. **FLOWERS** in spring and summer, sometimes off and on all year; 2 - 3" long, white to deep pink (very variable), very showy, in small axillary or terminal clusters on long branched stalks. **FRUIT** in summer, occasionally all year; quickly following the flowers; a brown cylindrical pod 3 - 5" long, rather narrow, with many small winged seeds. **FOUND** throughout the Bahamas, a common tree in all areas. A very dark flowered variety, on Inagua, is known as var. Inaguensis. Cuba. Bignoniaceae.

OPPOSITE LEAVES   WIDE BASE

    7. Veins prominent
      8. Leaf dull dark green, veins raised ....Darling Plum
      8. Leaf shiny bright green, soft ....Ironwood

DARLING PLUM

IRONWOOD

DARLING PLUM
REYNOSIA SEPTENTRIONALIS

10 - 20 feet. **TRUNK** slender to medium, straight, short. **CROWN** rather narrow, often regular, dense; branches erect, numerous. **BARK** gray to brown, thin, smooth on young trees, rough and furrowed with age. **TWIGS** gray to brown, slender, straight, roughened by lenticels and scattered leaf scars. **LEAVES** evergreen, firm, smooth, yellow-green to dark green and shiny above, slightly paler below; veins elevated; 1 - 2" long; stem very short; tip rounded, usually notched; base rounded. **FLOWERS** in spring and early summer; small, yellow-green, in short-stalked axillary clusters. **FRUIT** in summer and fall; about 1/2" across, round, smooth, black, dull, with thin green flesh (considered edible) and a large stone. **FOUND** throughout the Bahamas, as a shrub in scrubland and pine forest, and as a tree in mixed broadleaf areas. Florida. Rhamnaceae.

IRONWOOD
KRUGIODENDRON FERREUM

15 - 30 feet. **TRUNK** slender to medium, straight. **CROWN** narrow, generally regular, dense; branches erect. **BARK** light gray, thin, rough in furrows. **TWIGS** gray to light brown, slender, straight, smooth with occasional leaf scars. **LEAVES** evergreen, smooth, medium firm, bright to dark green and shiny above, paler below; net venation; 1/2 - 1 1/2" long; stem very short; tip rounded, often slightly notched; base rounded or wedge, margins wavy. **FLOWERS** in early summer; about 1/4" across, green, in small, very short-stalked clusters in leaf axils. **FRUIT** in late summer and fall; about 1/3" long, nearly round, black, smooth, shiny, sweet, edible. **FOUND** throughout the Bahamas; fairly common in mixed broadleaf areas. Florida, Jamaica, Cuba to St. Vincent. Rhamnaceae.

COMPOUND LEAVES UNBRANCHED STEMS

EVEN-NUMBERED LEAFLETS

1. Leaf with even numbered leaflets
   2. Leaf with two leaflets... Two Leaf
   2. Leaf with four or more leaflets
      3. Leaf with four leaflets..Inkwood
      3. Leaf with more than four leaflets
         4. Leaflets long pointed, leaflet midrib off centre
            5. Leaflets 4 - 8, 1 1/2 - 3" long, curved...................................... Mahogany
            5. Leaflets 16 - 32, 3 - 5" long ....Spanish Cedar

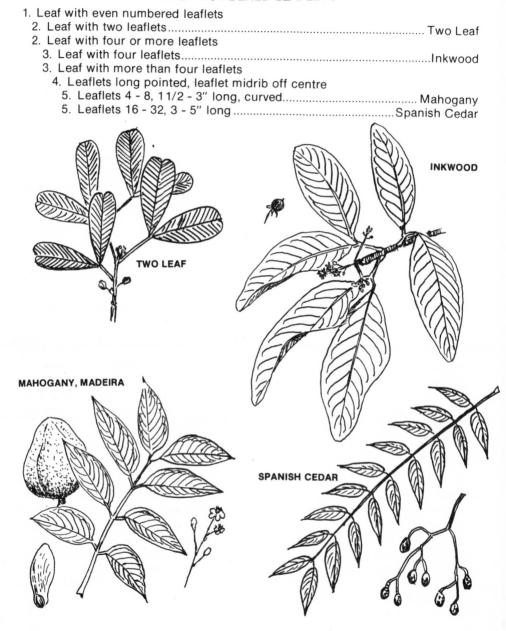

INKWOOD

TWO LEAF

MAHOGANY, MADEIRA

SPANISH CEDAR

TWO LEAF   ZANTHOXYLUM BIFOLIOLATUM

8 - 12 feet. **TRUNK** slender, short, sometimes armed at the base. **CROWN** somewhat spreading; branches slender, erect. **BARK** brown, thin, somewhat rough, cracking into small pieces. **TWIGS** brown to red-brown,medium thick, aromatic when broken. **LEAVES** alternate; 2, rarely 3, leaflets; evergreen, dark green and shiny above, paler below; prominent midrib and net venation; 1 - 2 1/2" long; stem about 1/2" long; tip notched, base unequal, margins recurved; leaf aromatic when crushed. **FLOWERS** in winter; tiny, pale green, single or few in small sessile axillary clusters. **FRUIT** not seen by authors. **FOUND** only on San Salvador; reasonably common there, in mixed broad-leaf areas. Cuba, Hispaniola. Rutaceae.

INKWOOD   EXOTHEA PANICULATA

20 - 50 feet. **TRUNK** medium, straight, tall. **CROWN** spreading, regular, dense; branches erect. **BARK** gray to light brown, often blotched, smooth, thin. **TWIGS** brown, slender, straight, roughened by lenticels. **LEAVES** alternate; 2 - 6 leaflets; smooth, medium firm, bright to dark green and shiny above, slightly paler below; net venation; 2 - 4" long; stem less than 1/4" long; tip short pointed, base wedge or round, margins generally wavy. **FLOWERS** in spring and early summer; about 1/3" across, numerous, showy, white, clustered at twig ends on branched stalks 1 - 3" long. **FRUIT** in summer and fall globose, about 1/2" across, dark purple to black, smooth, shiny. **FOUND** in Northern and Central Bahamas as one of the best and most common trees; in mixed broadleaf areas, sometimes in pinelands and scrub. Florida, Cuba, Jamaica, Hispaniola, Puerto Rico. Sapindaceae.

MAHOGANY   SWIETENIA MAHAGONI

20 - 50 feet. **TRUNK** medium to thick, straight. **CROWN** spreading, sometimes very much so, especially on older trees; branches erect to horizontal. **BARK** brown to dark brown, smooth; rough, furrowed, turning gray-brown with age. **TWIGS** brown, thick, rough with leaf scars. **LEAVES** alternate; 4 - 8 opposite pairs of leaflets; smooth, firm, yellow-green to dark green and shiny above, paler below; midrib prominent; 1 - 3" long; stem about 1/3" long; tip pointed, base unequal or wedge. **FLOWERS** in summer; tiny, numerous, yellow-green, on slender axillary stalks 2 - 3" long. **FRUIT** in winter; ovate, 3 - 5" long, green turning brown; erect, persistent, splitting at the bottom; each seed with one wing. **FOUND** throughout the Bahamas, relatively common; large trees in demand for lumber. Florida, West Indies, Mexico to Peru. Meliaceae.

SPANISH CEDAR   CEDRELA ODORATA

10 - 25 feet. **TRUNK** medium to large, straight. **CROWN** somewhat spreading, with large branches. **BARK** gray to brown, breaking into regular plates, the fissures showing brown. **TWIGS** gray, straight or slightly curved, with large light gray leaf scars. **LEAVES** alternate; 8 - 16 pairs of leaflets; dark green and shiny above, paler below; lateral veins prominent; 2 - 6" long; stem 1/4" long; tip long pointed, base blunt, margins smooth, sides slightly unequal; garlic odor when crushed. **FLOWERS** in spring and summer; small, yellow-green, numerous, in long terminal clusters. **FRUIT** in summer and fall; brown, elliptic, 1 1/2" long, 3/4" across; many small winged seeds. **FOUND** only on North Eleuthera; very rare. Jamaica, Honduras. Meliaceae.

COMPOUND LEAVES   UNBRANCHED STEMS

EVEN-NUMBERED LEAFLETS

4. Leaflets short pointed or round pointed
  5. Midrib off centre; leaflet short pointed..................................Lignum Vitae
  5. Midrib centred; leaflet tip rounded or notched
    6. Leaf dull, soft, 8 - 22 leaflets .... Mosquito Bush
    6. Leaf shiny
      7. Leaflets 4 - 8, notched, flat...Logwood
      7. Leaflets 4 - 14, rounded, margins curled ....Hercules Club

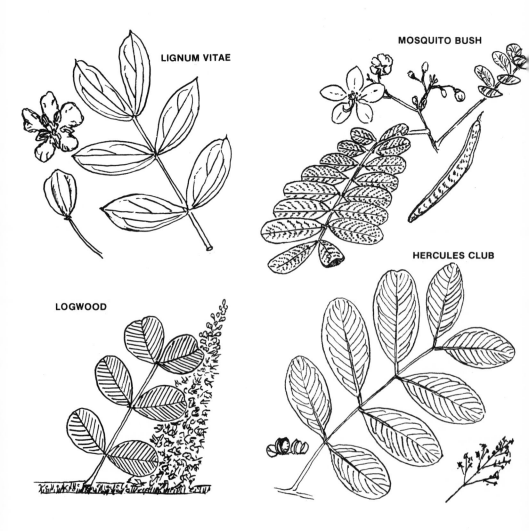

LIGNUM VITAE

MOSQUITO BUSH

HERCULES CLUB

LOGWOOD

LIGNUM VITAE   GUAIACUM SANCTUM

10 - 20 feet. **TRUNK** medium to thick, short, often twisted. **CROWN** spreading, medium dense; branches horizontal to erect. **BARK** light to dark gray, smooth on young trees, dark and irregularly furrowed with age. **TWIGS** green to gray, slender to medium, straight, roughened by lenticels. **LEAVES** opposite; 4 - 8 leaflets; evergreen, smooth, firm, dark green and somewhat shiny above, paler below; 1/2 - 1" long; tip and base unequal. **FLOWERS** in spring and early summer; about 2/3" across, blue-purple, showy; single or in small clusters on stalks 1 - 2" long at twig ends. **FRUITS** in summer and fall, sometimes winter; about 3/4" across, green turning orange, segments splitting to reveal several red-skinned black seeds. **FOUND** throughout the Bahamas, in mixed broadleaf and coastal areas. Florida, Cuba to Puerto Rico, Yucatan. Zygophyllaceae.

MOSQUITO BUSH   CASSIA BIFLORA

8 - 12 feet. **TRUNK** very slender, short. **CROWN** regular, medium dense; branches slender, erect. **BARK** dark brown, thin, smooth. **TWIGS** brown, slender, smooth, zig-zag. **LEAVES** alternate; 8 - 10 leaflets; smooth, dark green and dull above, much paler below; venation pinnate; 1/2 - 1" long; tip rounded or notched, base rounded or wedge. **FLOWERS** in fall and early winter; numerous, showy, about 1" across, bright yellow, on axillary and terminal stalks 1 1/2" long. **FRUIT** in winter; flat brown pod 2 - 4" long. **FOUND** in Central and Southern Bahamas, usually as a shrub of open areas; common. Florida, Jamaica, Cuba, Hispaniola, South America. Leguminosae.

LOGWOOD   HAEMATOXYLUM CAMPECHIANUM

15 - 30 feet. **TRUNK** medium to thick, short. **CROWN** spreading, regular, medium dense; branches medium to thick, horizontal to erect. **BARK** brown, thick, rough, breaking into irregular plates. **TWIGS** brown, straight or slightly zig-zag, medium thick, roughened by lenticels; occasionally a short spine or two in leaf axils. **LEAVES** alternate; 4 - 8 leaflets; medium firm, smooth, dark green and shiny above, slightly paler below; venation net, faint; 1/2 - 1" long; tip blunt or rounded, often notched; base wedge, often unequal. **FLOWERS** in winter and spring; about 1/2" across, numerous, showy, bright yellow, calyx brown, on axillary or terminal stalks 2 - 5" long; very fragrant. **FRUIT** in summer; flat, thin pod, 1 - 2" long, rather pointed at both ends, 1/2" wide. **FOUND** in Central Bahamas, in mixed broadleaf and cut-over areas. An early introduction, now naturalized, once valued for dye extracted from the heartwood. West Indies, Central America. Leguminosae.

HERCULES CLUB   ZANTHOXYLUM CORIACEUM

10 - 20 feet. **TRUNK** slender, short, sometimes armed at the base with pyramidal or conical spines. **CROWN** narrow, sometimes spreading, medium dense; branches erect. **BARK** dark brown, thick, furrowed. **TWIGS** dark brown, straight, thick, roughened by lines; sometimes with short, sharp axillary prickles; aromatic when broken. **LEAVES** alternate; 4 - 14 leaflets; evergreen, firm, smooth, dark green and shiny above, paler and sometimes with short, sharp, slender prockles below; net venation; 1 - 2" long; stem very short; tip rounded or blunt pointed, base wedge; leaf aromatic when crushed. **FLOWERS** in summer; small, pale green, in dense showy clusters at twig ends; fragrant. **FRUIT** in fall; about 1/8" across, globose, numerous, brown, dry, the seeds black, shiny. **FOUND** throughout the Bahamas, in mixed broadleaf areas; fairly common. Florida, Cuba, Hispaniola. Rutaceae.

COMPOUND LEAVES   UNBRANCHED STEMS

ODD-NUMBERED LEAFLETS

1. Leaf with odd numbered leaflets
    2. Leaf with three leaflets
        3. Leaflet with tip pointed
            4. Leaflet lacking a stem ....Three Leaf
            4. Leaflet stemmed.. White Torch
        3. Leaflet tip blunt pointed or rounded
            4. Leaflet and leaf on long stems
                5. Veins conspicuous..Bitter Wood
                5. Veins obscure.. Chicken Toe

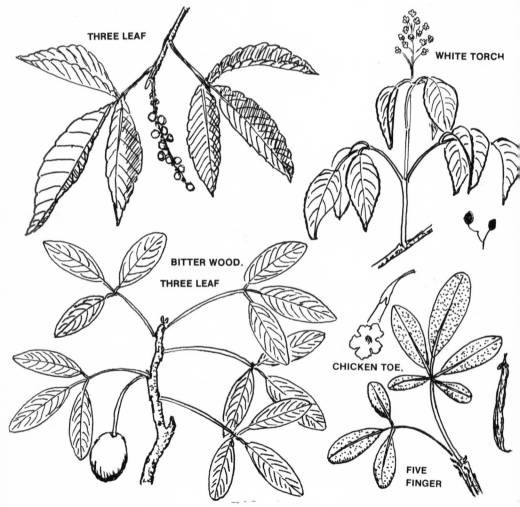

THREE LEAF

WHITE TORCH

BITTER WOOD.

THREE LEAF

CHICKEN TOE,

FIVE
FINGER

THREE LEAF
ALLOPHYLLUS COBBE

10 - 20 feet. **TRUNK** slender, short. **CROWN** somewhat spreading, open; branches slender, erect to drooping. **BARK** gray-brown, usually mottled, smooth, thin. **TWIGS** brown, straight, slender, smooth. **LEAVES** alternate; 3 leaflets; smooth, firm, bright green and shiny above, paler below; prominent midrib and pinnate venation; 2 - 4" long; stem very short; tip long pointed, base narrow, margins slightly wavy. **FLOWERS** in late summer and fall; less than 1/4" across, white, numerous, on terminal spikes 4 - 8" long. **FRUIT** in winter; about 1/8" across, bright red, numerous, globose, smooth, shiny. **FOUND** on New Providence and Abaco, usually an understory tree of mixed broadleaf areas; rather rare. Cuba, Hispaniola, Jamaica. Sapindaceae.

WHITE TORCH
AMYRIS ELEMIFERA

10 - 30 feet. **TRUNK** slender to medium, short. **CROWN** spreading, regular, medium dense; branches erect, numerous. **BARK** gray-brown, mottled, smooth, thin. **TWIGS** gray-brown, usually mottled, slender, smooth but for scattered leaf scars; aromatic when broken. **LEAVES** opposite; usually 3 leaflets, rarely 5; smooth, thin, medium firm, dark green and shiny above, much paler below; venation pinnate; 1 - 3" long; stem 1" or less; tip long pointed, base wedge; leaf aromatic when crushed. **FLOWERS** in fall and winter; small, numerous, white, fragrant, in large showy clusters at twig ends. **FRUIT** in winter and spring; about 1/4" across, round, smooth, green turning black, numerous. **FOUND** throughout the Bahamas, in mixed broadleaf areas. Florida, West Indies, Central America. Rutaceae.

BITTER WOOD
PICRODENDRON BACCATUM

10 - 20 feet. **TRUNK** thick, often crooked. **CROWN** spreading, very regular; branches erect, often crooked. **BARK** dark brown, thick, very rough, cracking into fissures and long strips. **TWIGS** brown, slender, straight, roughened, with lenticels and leaf scars. **LEAVES** alternate; 3 leaflets; firm, smooth, dark green and shiny above, lighter below; midrib prominent; 1 - 2" long; stem 1/2" long; tip blunt or rounded, base wedge. **FLOWERS** off and on all year, mainly in summer; male and female on different trees; both small and inconspicuous. **FRUIT** off and on all year, mainly in winter; oval, 1" long, yellow-orange, hanging from leaf axils on stalks 3 - 4" long, single or in twos and threes. **FOUND** in Northern and Central Bahamas, principally in mixed broadleaf areas; not common. Cuba. Picrodendraceae.

CHICKEN TOE
TABEBUIA BAHAMENSIS

20 - 50 feet. **TRUNK** slender to medium, straight, tall. **CROWN** narrow, sparse; branches short, erect. **BARK** brown to gray, thick, very rough in vertical furrows. **TWIGS** gray-brown, straight or slightly crooked, medium thick, roughened by numerous leaf scars. **LEAVES** with leaflet number variable from one to seven; smooth, firm, dark green and shiny above, pale gray-green below; midrib prominent, net venation; 1 - 3" long; stem 1/4 - 1" long; tip rounded or blunt, often notched, base rounded or wedge. **FLOWERS** in spring and summer, sometimes off and on all year; 2 - 3" long, white to deep pink (very variable), very showy, in small axillary or terminal clusters on long branched stalks. **FRUIT** in summer, occasionally all year; quickly following the flowers; a brown cylindrical pod 3 - 5" long, rather narrow, with many small winged seeds. **FOUND** throughout the Bahamas, a common tree in all areas. A very dark flowered variety, on Inagua, is known as var. Inague

COMPOUND LEAVES   UNBRANCHED STEMS

ODD-NUMBERED   LEAFLETS

   4. Leaflets on short stems
     5. Leaf long-stemmed, flexible ....White Ironwood
     5. Leaf short-stemmed, stiff .... Quicksilver Bush
 2. Leaf with three or more leaflets
   3. Leaflets palmate in arrangement, 3 - 5....................................... Chicken Toe
   3. Leaflets not palmate in arrangement
     4. Leafstem winged.. Wild Lime

WHITE IRONWOOD   **QUICKSILVER BUSH, HARD BARK, NAKED WOOD**

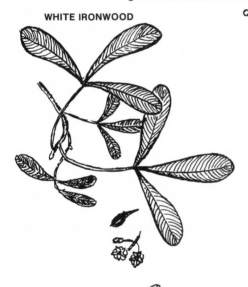

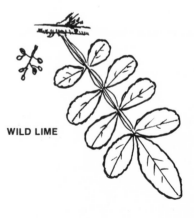

WILD LIME

CHICKEN TOE, FIVE FINGER

WHITE IRONWOOD   HYPELATE TRIFOLIATA

15 - 40 feet. **TRUNK** medium, straight. **CROWN** somewhat spreading, medium dense; branches erect. **BARK** gray-brown, occasionally dark brown, often mottled; smooth on young trees, cracking into small pieces with age. **TWIGS** gray-brown, blotched, slender, straight or curved, smooth except for old leaf scars. **LEAVES** alternate; 3 leaflets; smooth, firm, bright to dark green and shiny above, slightly paler below; fairly prominent midrib, pinnate venation; 1 - 2 1/2" long; stem very short; tip rounded or notched, base narrow or wedge. **FLOWERS** in spring or summer; less than 1/4" across, pale green, on small branched clusters on slender axillary or terminal stalk 1 - 3" long. **FRUIT** in spring and summer; 1/4" or less across, black, ovoid. **FOUND** throughout the Bahamas, in mixed broadleaf areas; widespread, but not generally common. Florida, Jamaica, Cuba to Puerto Rico. Sapindaceae.

QUICKSILVER   THOUINIA DISCOLOR

15 - 35 feet. **TRUNK** slender to medium, straight, tall. **CROWN** narrow, medium dense; branches short, erect. **BARK** brown, often blotched; smooth, when young, thin and cracking with age. **TWIGS** brown, straight or slightly curved, medium thick, rough with old leaf scars. **LEAVES** alternate; 1 - 3 leaflets; medium firm, smooth, dark yellow-green and somewhat shiny above, much paler and dull below; venation pinnate; 3/4 - 3" long; stem 1/4" long or less; tip rounded or notched, base wedge or narrow. **FLOWERS** in fall, winter, or spring; small, white, numerous, on terminal spike 1" long or more. **FRUIT** in winter, spring, or summer; brown, wafer-thin, papery, 1/3" long and 1/8" wide. **FOUND** throughout the Bahamas, very common in mixed broadleaf areas and scrubland. Sapindaceae.

WILD LIME   ZANTHOXYLUM FAGARA

10 - 25 feet. **TRUNK** slender, short. **CROWN** somewhat spreading, often regular, medium dense; branches erect, numerous, armed with curved prickles 1/3" long. **BARK** gray to brown, thin, smooth, slightly roughened with age. **TWIGS** green to gray, slender, smooth, slightly zig-zag, usually armed with a pair of short sharp prickles in the axils. **LEAVES** alternate; 5 - 11 leaflets; smooth, medium firm, bright to dark green and shiny above, paler and somewhat shiny below; 1/4 - 1" long; stem very short; tip rounded, blunt, or notched, base wedge or rounded, margins smooth or somewhat serrate; leafstem winged; leaf aromatic when crushed. **FLOWERS** in spring and early summer; very small, pale green, fragrant, in dense short-stalked clusters in the leaf axils, male and female on different trees. **FRUIT** in summer and fall; about 1/8" across, round, rust-brown, opening to reveal one or two small, shiny black seeds. **FOUND** throughout the Bahamas, but apparently not on Abaco; fairly common in mixed broadleaf areas. Scent of crushed leaves that of citrus. Florida, West Indies, Texas, Mexico, Central and South America. Rutaceae.

CHICKEN TOE   TABEBUIA BAHAMENSIS

20 - 50 feet. **TRUNK** slender to medium, straight, tall. **CROWN** narrow, sparse; branches short, erect. **BARK** brown to gray, thick, very rough in vertical furrows. **TWIGS** gray-brown, straight or slightly crooked, medium thick, roughened by numerous leaf scars. **LEAVES** with leaflet number variable from one to seven; smooth, firm, dark green and shiny above, pale gray-green below; midrib prominent, net venation; 1 - 3" long; stem 1/4 - 1" long; tip rounded or blunt, often notched, base rounded or wedge. **FLOWERS** in spring and summer, sometimes off and on all year; 2 - 3" long, white to deep pink (very variable), very showy, in small axillary or terminal clusters on long branched stalks. **FRUIT** in summer, occasionally all year; quickly following the flowers; a brown cylindrical pod 3 - 5" long, rather narrow, with many small winged seeds. **FOUND** throughout the Bahamas, a common tree in all areas. A very dark flowered variety, on Inagua, is known as var. Inaguensis. Cuba. Bignoniaceae.

COMPOUND LEAVES   UNBRANCHED STEMS

ODD-NUMBERED LEAFLETS

4. Leafstem not winged
   5. Leaflets 5 - 9, not opposite each other ....Snakeroot
   5. Leaflets opposite each other
      6. Leaflets narrowed at the base
         7. Midrib white, thick; tip pointed ....Boar Gum-Elemi
         7. Midrib green, no tiny point at leaf tip
            8. Leaflets shiny, 3 - 9 ....Cuban Yellow Wood
            8. Leaflets dull, 5 - 11 ....Stinking Pea Root

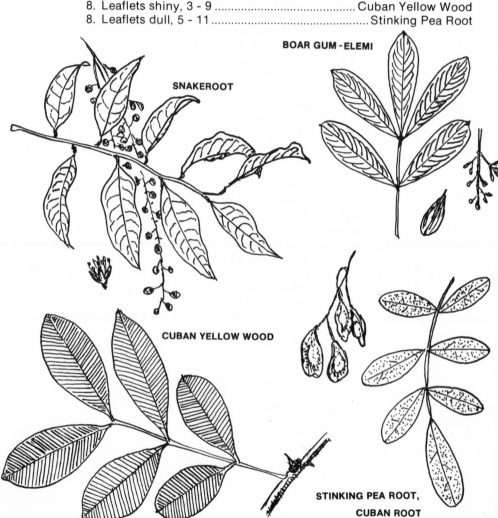

BOAR GUM-ELEMI

SNAKEROOT

CUBAN YELLOW WOOD

STINKING PEA ROOT,
CUBAN ROOT

SNAKE ROOT
PICRAMNIA PENTANDRA

10 - 20 feet. **TRUNK** slender, straight. **CROWN** spreading, rather open; branches slender, arching. **BARK** brown, often mottled, smooth, thin. **TWIGS** brown, straight or a little curved, slender, more or less smooth. **LEAVES** alternate; 5 - 9 leaflets; medium firm and smooth, dark green and shiny above, paler below; net venation prominent; 2 - 5" long; stem 1/8" long; tip long pointed, base wedge or sometimes unequal; margins often wavy. **FLOWERS** in summer; male and female on different trees; both small, pale green, in small clusters on stalks 5 - 8" long at twig ends. **FRUIT** in fall, winter, and spring; elliptic, 1/3 - 1/2" long, smooth, shiny dark red, showy, quite numerous. **FOUND** throughout the Bahamas, but apparently not on Inagua; common in mixed broadleaf areas. Florida, Cuba to Trinidad. Simaroubaceae.

BOAR GUM ELEMI
BURSERA INAGUENSIS

8 - 15 feet, often a shrub. **TRUNK** medium to thick, short. **CROWN** spreading, medium dense or sparse; branches erect, brittle. **BARK** gray to brown, often mottled, smooth, thin but not peeling; aromatic when cut. **TWIGS** red-brown, slender to medium, curved, smooth; aromatic when broken. **LEAVES** alternate; 3 - 7 leaflets; smooth, thin, dark green and shiny above, paler below; 1 - 2" long; stem very short; tip short pointed, base wedge; aromatic when crushed. **FLOWERS** in summer; less than 1/4" across, cream coloured, numerous, on long axillary stalks. **FRUIT** in fall and winter; 1/4 - 1/3" across, globose, red-brown, smooth. **FOUND** in Southern Bahamas and Cat Island, in scrubland and low mixed broadleaf areas; common in some places, especially so on Inagua. Islands off north Cuba coast. Burseraceae.

CUBAN YELLOW WOOD
ZANTHOXYLUM CUBENSE

8 - 12 feet, usually a shrub. **TRUNK** slender, short, thickly covered with short sharp pyramidal or conical spines. **CROWN** narrow or sparse; branches erect, few. **BARK** gray to dark brown, thin, smooth, sometimes with vertical fissures showing red underbark. **TWIGS** green to brown, slender, straight, smooth, usually with short, sharp axillary prickles; aromatic when broken. **LEAVES** alternate; 3 - 9 leaflets; evergreen, firm, smooth, dark green and shiny above, much paler and with several slender prickles 1/3" long below; prominent midrib; 3/4 - 1 1/2" long; almost stemless; tip short or blunt pointed, base wedge; leaf aromatic when crushed. **FLOWERS** in spring, summer, and fall; less than 1/8" across, numerous, round, brown, dry. **FOUND** on South Andros only; occurring in pineland or mixed broadleaf areas; very rare. Cuba. Rutaceae.

STINKING PEA ROOT
ATELIA GUMMIFERA

10 - 30 feet. **TRUNK** slender to medium, straight. **CROWN** generally narrow, occasionally spreading, regular; branches erect. **BARK** gray, sometimes blotched, smooth, thin, becoming somewhat cracked and rough on older trees. **TWIGS** gray, straight, medium thick, sometimes slightly crooked, smooth but for leaf scars. **LEAVES** alternate; 7 - 9 leaflets; smooth, medium firm, dark green and somewhat shiny above, paler below; venation obscure; 3/4 - 2" long; tip rounded or blunt, base rounded or wedge, sometimes unequal. **FLOWERS** in fall; small, pale green, numerous, on long branched terminal spikes. **FRUIT** in winter; 1/3" across, light brown, thin, dry, papery, numerous. **FOUND** in Central Bahamas, a shrub of pinelands and a small tree in mixed broadleaf areas; common in some areas. Unpleasant odor when root is broken. Cuba. Leguminosae.

COMPOUND LEAVES   UNBRANCHED STEMS
              ODD-NUMBERED   LEAFLETS

6. Leaflets broad or obtuse at the base
   7. Leaflets 3 - 11; low, dull teeth .... Satin Wood
   7. Leaflets without teeth
      8. Leaflets 5 (3 - 7), widest at base .... Poison Wood
     8. Leaflets widest near midpoint or tip
        9. Leaflets 7 - 11, rounded; bark gray .... Dogwood
        9. Leaflets 5 - 7, pointed; bark red .... Gum-Elemi

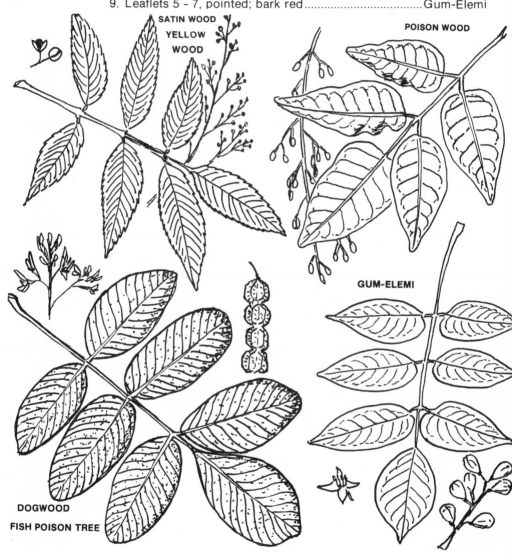

SATIN WOOD
YELLOW WOOD

POISON WOOD

DOGWOOD
FISH POISON TREE

GUM-ELEMI

SATIN WOOD — ZANTHOXYLUM FLAVUM

10 - 25 feet. **TRUNK** medium, straight. **CROWN** spreading, regular, not dense; branches medium, erect. **BARK** gray, usually very blotched, smooth, thin; aromatic when cut. **TWIGS** gray, medium thick, straight, smooth; aromatic when broken. **LEAVES** alternate; 3 - 7 leaflets; smooth, firm, yellow-green and shiny above, slightly paler below; midvein prominent; small translucent dots on both surfaces; 1 - 2" long; stem red or yellow, less than 1/4" long; tip blunt pointed, base unequal, margins smooth or slightly dentate; leaf aromatic when crushed. **FLOWERS** in summer and fall; male and female on different trees; both very small, numerous, cream coloured, on axillary stalks 3 - 4" long. **FRUIT** in fall and winter; small, numerous, round, splitting open, 1 - 2 shiny black seeds. **FOUND** throughout the Bahamas, in scrubland and mixed broadleaf areas; the wood is highly prized, hence tree rare except on Inagua. Bermuda, Florida, Cuba, Santo Domingo to St. Lucia. Rutaceae.

POISON WOOD — METOPIUM TOXIFERUM

20 - 50 feet. **TRUNK** medium to thick, short to tall. **CROWN** spreading to open; branches medium to thick, horizontal to erect. **BARK** light gray-brown, mottled, becoming orange-brown and mottled with age, thin and cracking on older trees; when cut, gives off a while, poisonous sap that dries black. **TWIGS** brown, thick, straight or a little crooked, smooth except for leaf scars; when broken, gives off a white, poisonous sap. **LEAVES** alternate; 5 - 7 leaflets; medium firm, smooth, dark green and shiny above, paler below; net venation; 1 1/2 - 3 1/2" long; stem 1/2" long; tip rounded or blunt pointed, base heart shape or rounded; surface may be covered with small black dots. **FLOWERS** in spring and early summer; small, numerous, cream coloured, on branched axillary stalks 7 - 10" long. **FRUIT** in summer and fall; orange-brown, 3/4" long, ovate, smooth, numerous; poisonous if eaten. **FOUND** throughout the Bahamas, as a tree or a shrub; common, a most attractive tree. The antidote to skin irritation is the sap of the Gumelemi. Florida, Cuba, Haiti, Puerto Rico. Anacardiaceae.

DOGWOOD — PISCIDIA PISCIPULA

20 - 50 feet. **TRUNK** medium to thick, straight. **CROWN** spreading, somewhat irregular, medium dense; branches medium erect. **BARK** gray, thin, smooth, often faintly brown-blotched; rough, fissured with age. **TWIGS** gray to brown, thick, zig-zag, smooth, with numerous lenticels. **LEAVES** alternate; 7 - 9 leaflets; smooth, firm, dark green and shiny above, pale gray-green below; midrib prominent, venation pinnate; 1 1/2 - 4" long; stem thick, 1/4" long; tip short pointed or rounded, base wedge or rounded, margins often re-curved. **FLOWERS** in early summer, before the new leaves; numerous, showy, white tinged with pink and purple, about 3/4" long, in short-stalked clusters along the twigs. **FRUIT** in summer; medium brown flat pods 3 - 4" long, 1" wide. **FOUND** throughout the Bahamas, but apparently not on Inagua; relatively common; the wood used in boat building; bark and leaves, when pulped, make a fish poison. Florida, West Indies, tropical America. Leguminosae.

GUM ELEMI — BURSERA SIMARUBA

20 - 50 feet. **TRUNK** medium to thick, straight. **CROWN** spreading, medium dense; branches thick, brittle, erect. **BARK** red-brown, occasionally gray, very thin and usually peeling especially on older trees. **TWIGS** gray to brown, smooth, thick, a few lenticels; aromatic when broken. **LEAVES** alternate, deciduous; 3 - 9 leaflets; smooth, medium firm, dark green and shiny above, paler below; net venation; 1 - 3" long; stem 1/2" long or less, that of end leaflet 1"; tip short to long pointed, base wedge, often unequal; leaf aromatic when crushed. **FLOWERS** in spring and early summer, just before the new leaves; very small, pale green, fragrant, on stalks 2 - 5" long. **FRUIT** in summer and fall; green turning dark red; 1/3 - 1/2" long, 1/3" across, rather numerous, persistent. **FOUND** throughout the Bahamas, common; living fences made by placing end of branch in the ground. Florida, West Indies, tropical America. Burseraceae.

COMPOUND LEAVES   UNBRANCHED STEMS
ODD-NUMBERED LEAFLETS

3. Leaf with usually more than 11 leaflets
    4. Leaflets 7 - 21; shiny dark green above ....Paradise Tree
    4. Leaflets 25 or more
        5. Leaflets toothed, 25 - 35; margins curled ....Low Spathelia
        5. Leaflets not toothed; margins flat
            6. Leaflets generally over 1" long, hairy.............................Coast Sophora
            6. Leaflets under 1" long, not hairy .... Alvaradoa

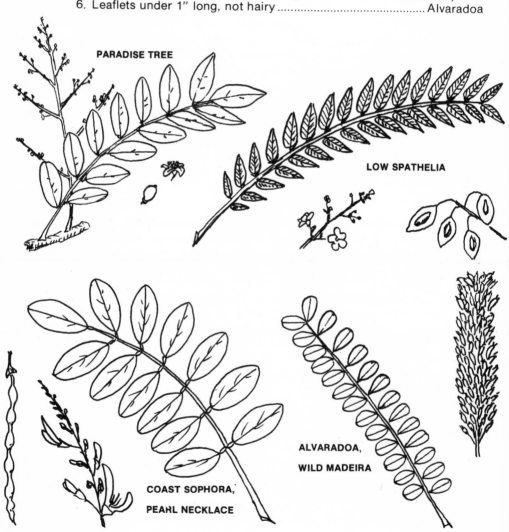

PARADISE TREE

LOW SPATHELIA

COAST SOPHORA,
PEARL NECKLACE

ALVARADOA,
WILD MADEIRA

PARADISE TREE   SIMAROUBA GLAUCA

15 - 40 feet. **TRUNK** medium to thick, tall, straight. **CROWN** regular, often spreading, not dense; branches erect or horizontal. **BARK** gray to brown, thick, smooth, becoming slightly cracked with age. **TWIGS** brown, thick, straight, roughened by leaf scars. **LEAVES** alternate; 6 - 12 leaflets; thin, medium firm, dark green, smooth and very shiny above, pale green and slightly downy below; prominent midrib, delicate pinnate venation; 1 1/2 - 3 1/2" long; stem medium thick, 1/4" long or less; tip rounded or notched, base unequal or wedge. **FLOWERS** in spring and early summer; 1/4" across. numerous, yellow-green, on many branched terminal spikes 10 - 15" long; male and female on different trees. **FRUIT** in summer; 1" long, smooth, shiny, red turning dark purple, ovate. **FOUND** in Northern and Central Bahamas, but apparently not on Cat Island, Exuma, nor San Salvador; in mixed broadleaf areas, moderately common, attractive. Florida, Cuba, Hispaniola, Jamaica, Mexico to Panama. Simaroubaceae.

LOW SPATHELIA   SPATHELIA VERNICOSA

8 - 10 feet, often a shrub. **TRUNK** slender, upright or slightly leaning. **CROWN** narrow and dense; branches few, short, with prominent leaf scars. **BARK** brown, thin, somewhat fissured. **TWIGS** light brown to green, smooth, slender. **LEAVES** alternate. clustered at twig ends; 25 - 35 leaflets; smooth, medium firm, dark green and shiny above, much lighter below; midrib prominent; 1 - 2" long, almost linear; tip rounded or blunt, base rounded, margins serrate. **FLOWERS** in summer; small, showy, numerous. dark red, on very long, much branched stalks 1 - 3 feet long at twig ends. **FRUIT** in winter; green turning brown and drying, 1/3" across, oval, smooth, numerous. **FOUND** on S. Eleuthera and Cat Island, in scrubland and mixed broadleaf areas; often dying back after fruiting, to spring up again from the rootstock. Cuba. Rutaceae.

SOPHORA   SOPHORA TOMENTOSA

8 - 10 feet, more often a shrub. **TRUNK** thin, short, sometimes multiple. **CROWN** generally spreading and open; branches slender, numerous. **BARK** gray to black, smooth, thin. **TWIGS** green to gray, rather thick, smooth, slightly downy. **LEAVES** alternate; 11 - 17 leaflets; smooth, firm, dark green and shiny above, paler below; very fine net venation; 3/4 - 1 1/2" long; stem short, pale pink; tip rounded, base rounded or abruptly wedge. **FLOWERS** in summer and fall; bright yellow, about 3/4" long. very numerous on thick terminal stalk 8 - 12" long. **FRUIT** in fall and winter; cylindrical thin brown pod 2 - 4" long. **FOUND** throughout the Bahamas, in coastal areas, occasionally inland. Bermuda, Florida, Jamaica, Cuba to St. Vincent, Old World tropics. Leguminosae.

ALVARADOA   ALVARADOA AMORPHOIDES

15 - 40 feet. **TRUNK** slender to medium, straight, tall. **CROWN** rather narrow, sparse to medium dense; branches erect. **BARK** brown, thin, smooth, slightly roughened with age. **TWIGS** gray to brown, smooth, slender. **LEAVES** alternate; leaflets numerous; smooth, thin, dark green and dull above, light gray-green below; midrib prominent; 1/2" long; tip rounded, base rounded or wedge; leaf turning purple with age. **FLOWERS** in fall and early winter; numerous, very small, yellow-green, fuzzy, on drooping spikes 3" long or more. **FRUIT** in winter and spring; about 1/4" long, numerous, a samara with 2 - 3 wings, pointed at the tip, yellow-green tinged with brown. **FOUND** in Central Bahamas, but not on San Salvador, in mixed broadleaf areas. Florida, Cuba, Mexico. Simaroubaceae.

COMPOUND LEAVES   BRANCHING STEMS

A. Leaf with one pair of branching stems
    1. Leaflets with stems ....Cat's Claw, Ram's Horn, Bahama Cat's Claw
    1. Leaflets without stems..Casinas, Pork and Doughboy

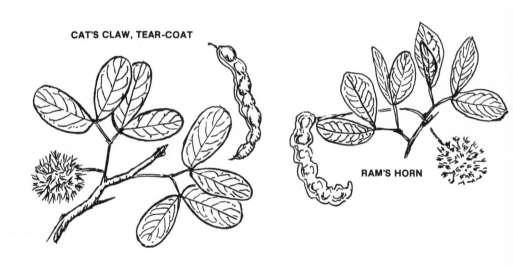

CAT'S CLAW, TEAR-COAT

RAM'S HORN

BAHAMA CAT'S CLAW, TEAR-COAT

CASINAS

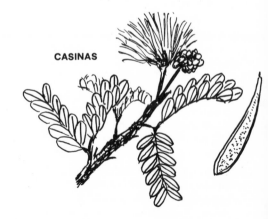

CAT'S CLAW   PITHECELLOBIUM UNGUIS-CATI

6 - 10 feet. **TRUNK** slender, very short. **CROWN** spreading and irregular; branches erect, long, armed with straight spines 1/4" long. **BARK** brown, thin, slightly rough and cracking into small pieces. **TWIGS** brown, slender, straight or zig-zag, slightly roughened by numerous lenticels; with straight spines 1/4" long. **LEAVES** alternate; 2 - 4 leaflets; smooth, medium firm, dark green and slightly shiny above, paler and dull below; net venation; 1/2 - 2" long; tip rounded, sometimes unequal; base unequal; leaf-stem longer than leaflet stems. **FLOWERS** in fall and spring; minute, showy, in dense pink to dark pink heads about 3/4" across, turning brown when dry. **FRUIT** in winter and summer; brown flat pod 2 - 4" long, irregularly coiled around dark seeds in red flesh. **FOUND** on San Salvador and Southern Bahamas. Florida, West Indies, Yucatan, South America. Leguminosae.

RAM'S HORN   PITHECELLOBIUM GUADELUPENSE

10 - 20 feet. **CROWN** slender to medium, short, crooked, rarely multiple. **CROWN** irregular, medium dense; branches numerous, twisted. **BARK** brown, thin and smooth on young trees, in shallow fissures with age. **TWIGS** brown, slender, generally short and crooked, roughened by lenticels and leaf scars, with some short spines in the axils. **LEAVES** alternate; 2 - 4 leaflets; net venation; 1/2 - 2" long; tip rounded or blunt, base wedge or unequal; leaflet stems longer than leaf stems. **FLOWERS** in fall and spring; minute, numerous, in dense round heads 3/4" across, pale pink, on axillary stalks 3" long or more, turning brown when dry. **FRUIT** in winter and summer; very curved flat brown pod 2 - 4" long, round dark seeds in red flesh. **FOUND** throughout the Bahamas. Florida, Cuba, Leguminosae.

BAHAMA CAT'S CLAW   PITHECELLOBIUM BAHAMENSE

8 - 12 feet, sometimes a shrub. **TRUNK** slender, short. **CROWN** spreading, open, irregular; branches erect, occasionally drooping. **BARK** gray to brown, thin, smooth. **TWIGS** brown, slender, zig-zag, with short, rigid spines 1/4" long in the axils, usually in pairs. **LEAVES** alternate; 2 - 4 leaflets; firm, smooth, dark green and shiny above, paler below; 1/3 - 1" long; tip rounded or blunt, base wedge or unequal; leaf stems longer than leaflet stems. **FLOWERS** in fall and spring; very small, numerous, bright to dark pink. in dense round heads about 3/4" across, on axillary stalk 1" long or more, turning brown when dry. **FRUIT** winter and summer; flat, dark brown pod 2 - 4" long, irregularly coiled around dark seeds in red flesh. **FOUND** in Central Bahamas, usually in pinelands. Cuba. Leguminosae.

CASINAS   CALLIANDRA HAEMATOMMA

10 - 15 feet. **TRUNK** slender, short. **CROWN** irregular, spreading, open; branches arching. **BARK** gray-brown to dark brown, thin, slightly roughened by scars of old branches. **TWIGS** brown, slender, straight, somewhat roughened by numerous lenticels and old leaf scars; when young, armed with many short spines. **LEAVES** alternate; 10 - 20 leaflets; thin, smooth, dark green and shiny above, paler below; 1/8 - 1/3" long; tip blunt or rounded, base wedge or rounded. **FLOWERS** off and on all year, mainly in fall and early winter; very small, numerous, medium red, in showy heads about 1" long at twig ends or axillary. **FRUIT** off and on all year, mainly winter and spring; pod slightly curved, flat, 2 - 3" long, rather narrow, turning brown and splitting open. **FOUND** on Grand Bahama, Abaco, San Salvador, and Inagua, in mixed broadleaf areas and scrublands. Cuba to Virgin Islands. Leguminosae.

COMPOUND LEAVES   BRANCHING STEMS

B. Leaf with one to three pairs of branching stems.............Horseflesh, Cinnecord

C. Leaf with two to three pairs of branching stems ....Brasiletto

PORK-AND-DOUGHBOY, ROSEWOOD, BAHAMA ACACIA

HORSEFLESH

CINNECORD

BRASILETTO

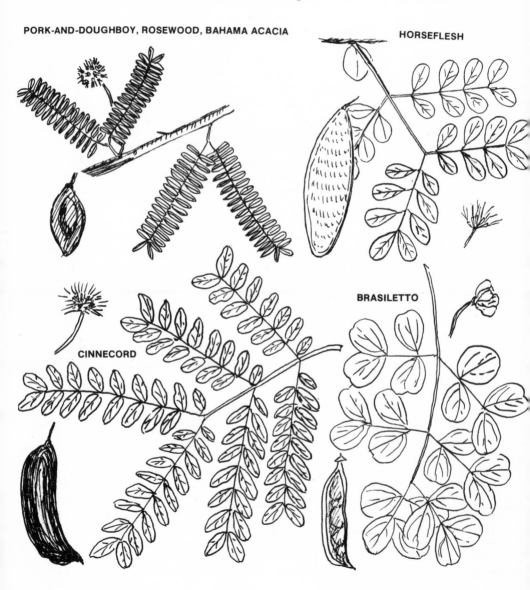

PORK AND DOUGHBOY   ACACIA ACUIFERA

8 - 15 feet, often a shrub. **TRUNK** slender to medium, short; sometimes armed with clusters of stiff spines 1 1/2 - 4" long at the base. **CROWN** spreading, irregular; branches medium, sometimes with 1 - 2 stiff spines 1" long or more. **BARK** gray to brown, thin, splitting into small pieces on older trees. **TWIGS** brown, slender, curved or straight, roughened by lenticels, often with slender spines 1/8" long in the axils, single or paired. **LEAVES** alternate; 8 - 17 pairs of leaflets; smooth, firm, dark green and shiny above, paler below; 1/4 - 3/4" long; tip and base rounded. **FLOWERS** in spring and early summer; individually very small, in dense, globose, bright yellow heads about 1/3" across, on axillary stalk 1" long. **FRUIT** in summer; slender, curved, almost cylindrical, thin brown pod 2 - 3" long. **FOUND** throughout the Bahamas, but apparently not on New Providence, San Salvador, nor Mayaguana; attains largest size on Inagua. Leguminosae.

HORSEFLESH   LYSILOMA SABICU

20 - 50 feet. **TRUNK** medium to thick, straight, tall. **CROWN** spreading, medium dense or rather open; branches medium, erect. **BARK** gray-brown to brown, very rough, breaking into long irregular strips. **TWIGS** brown, slender to medium, somewhat roughened by many pale lenticels. **LEAVES** alternate; leaflets numerous; smooth, firm, thin, dark green and dull above, paler below; 1/2 - 1" long; tip blunt or rounded, base unequal or wedge; leaflets dark red when very young. **FLOWERS** in early summer, occasionally in fall; very small, in showy, dense white heads about 1" across, on axillary stalk 2 - 3" long. **FRUIT** in summer, sometimes through the year; persistent, brown, flat, somewhat twisted pod 3 - 4" long, 1 1/2" wide, **FOUND** in Central Bahamas, in high and low mixed broadleaf areas; wood prized for boat building. Cuba. Hispaniola. Leguminosae.

CINNECORD   ACACIA CHORIOPHYLLA

15 - 35 feet. **TRUNK** medium to thick, straight, sometimes leaning. **CROWN** spreading, medium dense; branches medium, erect. **BARK** light gray to brown, often heavily blotched with black; smooth when young, thick and rough with fissures and scales when older. **TWIGS** brown, slender, straight or somewhat zig-zag, lightly roughened by lenticels and faint horizontal lines. **LEAVES** alternate; leaflets numerous; smooth, firm, dark green and shiny above, slightly paler below; venation not conspicuous; 1/3 - 1/2" long; tip and base rounded. **FLOWERS** in spring and early summer; minute, numerous, showy, bright yellow, in dense round heads about 1/2" across, on axillary stalk 2 - 3" long. **FRUIT** in summer; dark brown, rather thick pod 2 - 3" long; turning darker, with several black, shiny seeds. **FOUND** throughout the Bahamas, growing in all areas. Islands north of Cuba. Leguminosae.

BRASILETTO   CAESALPINIA VESICARIA

10 - 25 feet. **TRUNK** slender to medium, straight or crooked. **CROWN** regular, medium dense; branches erect, numerous. **BARK** gray to brown, sometimes covered with short pyramidal or conical spines that dull and vanish with age, the bark then fissuring. **TWIGS** gray to brown, slender, straight, smooth or armed with a few prickles 1/4" long. **LEAVES** alternate; leaflets numerous; firm, smooth, dark green and shiny above, paler below; inconspicuous net venation; 1/2 - 1 1/2" long; stem very short; tip blunt, rounded, or notched; base wedge or rounded; margins somewhat recurved. **FLOWERS** off and on all year, mainly in summer and fall; numerous, very showy, bright yellow, on single or compound terminal or axillary stalks 5 - 10" long. **FRUIT** off and on all year, mainly summer and fall; brown, slender, flat pod 3 - 6" long. **FOUND** on Andros, Exuma, and Long Island, in scrublands and mixed broadleaf areas; not common. Cuba, Jamaica, Yucatan. Leguminosae.

COMPOUND LEAVES   BRANCHING STEMS

D. Leaf with two to four pairs of branching stems...Brasiletto, Bahama Haulback
E. Leaf with two to five pairs of branching stems............................Wild Tamarind
F. Leaf with three to four pairs of branching stems ....Blue Seed

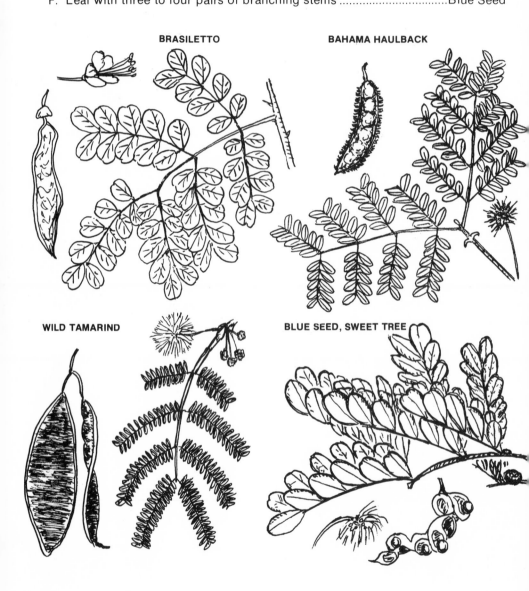

BRASILETTO   **BAHAMA HAULBACK**

WILD TAMARIND   **BLUE SEED, SWEET TREE**

BRASILETTO
CAESALPINIA BAHAMENSIS

10 - 25 feet. **TRUNK** slender to medium, short, straight or crooked. **CROWN** narrow, medium dense; erect branches covered with short conical or pyramidal spines. **BARK** gray to brown, spiny, the spines disappearing with age; rough on old trees. **TWIGS** gray slender, smooth but for short, slender prickles. **LEAVES** alternate; leaflets numerous; smooth, thin, medium firm, dark green and shiny above, much paler below; net venation; 1/2 - 1 1/2" long; tip rounded, blunt, or notched, base rounded or slightly narrowed. **FLOWERS** in spring or throughout the year; showy, yellow-green, with several stamens about 1" long, in long-stalked, much branched clusters at twig ends. **FRUIT** in early summer or throughout the year; brown, flat, slightly curved pod 3 - 4" long, less than 1/2" wide. **FOUND** throughout the Bahamas, commonly a shrub in pinelands and a tree in mixed broadleaf areas. A spineless race (var. reticulata) grows on Great Abaco, Grand Bahama, and Inagua. Cuba. Leguminosae.

BAHAMA HAULBACK
MIMOSA BAHAMENSIS

6 - 10 feet. **TRUNK** slender to medium, often multiple. **CROWN** spreading, very dense; branches numerous, armed with hooked prickles about 1/4" long. **BARK** brown, thin, vertically furrowed. **TWIGS** red-brown, slender, smooth, slightly curved, armed with hooked prickles 1/8" long. **LEAVES** alternate; leaflets numerous; smooth, thin, medium firm, dark green and dull above, paler below; 1/8 - 1/3" long; tip and base more or less rounded. **FLOWERS** in fall and early winter; very small, numerous, in round, dense. showy pink heads about 1/2" across, on short axillary stalks. **FRUIT** in winter and spring; showy, red-brown pods, 1 - 2" long and 1/3" wide, flat, slightly curved, with tiny prickles along the edge. **FOUND** on San Salvador and the Southern Bahamas, common in scrublands and cut-over land; beautiful when in flower, but a perfect devil to encounter. Leguminosae.

WILD TAMARIND
LYSILOMA LATISILIQUUM

20 - 50 feet. **TRUNK** medium to thick, short to tall. **CROWN** spreading, medium dense; branches medium to large, erect to horizontal. **BARK** gray, smooth, thin when young, furrowed with age and cracking into thin pieces, almost black. **TWIGS** gray to brown, zig-zag, slender, smooth. **LEAVES** alternate; leaflets numerous; thin, smooth, bright to dark green and shiny above, paler below; 1/3 - 1/2" long; tip short pointed or rounded, base unequal; young leaflets red-brown. **FLOWERS** in spring or early summer, sometimes in fall minute, numerous, in dense, showy round heads about 2/3" across, on axillary stalks 2 - 3" long. **FRUIT** in summer to early winter; dark brown, very flat, slightly twisted pod, often peeling, 4 - 5" long and 1 1/2 - 2" wide. **FOUND** throughout the Bahamas; one of the commonest and largest trees. Florida, Cuba, Yucatan. Leguminosae.

BLUE SEED
PITHECELLOBIUM GLAUCUM

10 - 25 feet. **TRUNK** slender to medium, straight. **CROWN** spreading, regular, dense; branches erect to horizontal, crooked. **BARK** pale gray, thin, smooth. **TWIGS** light gray, slender, straight, slightly roughened by leaf scars. **LEAVES** opposite; leaflets numerous; smooth, medium firm, very dark green and shiny above, slightly paler below; midrib prominent; 1/2 - 1" long; tip rounded or notched, base rounded. **FLOWERS** in spring or early summer, occasionally all year; numerous, minute, white, in dense round heads about 3/4" wide, on axillary or terminal stalks about 1/4" long. **FRUIT** in summer and fall, occasionally all year; dark brown, flat, curling pod 2 - 3" long, opening to reveal several showy, persistent blue seeds 1/4" long. **FOUND** on Abaco and South Andros, in mixed broadleaf areas and pinelands; very attractive. Cuba. Leguminosae.

COMPOUND LEAVES   BRANCHING STEMS

G. Leaf with three to eight pairs of branching stems......................... Swwt Acacia

H. Leaf with three to ten pairs of branching stems......................................Jumbay

I. Leaf with six to twelve pairs of branching stems.............................Sarah's Toe

J. Leaf with eight to forty pairs of branching stems.............. Acacia macracantha

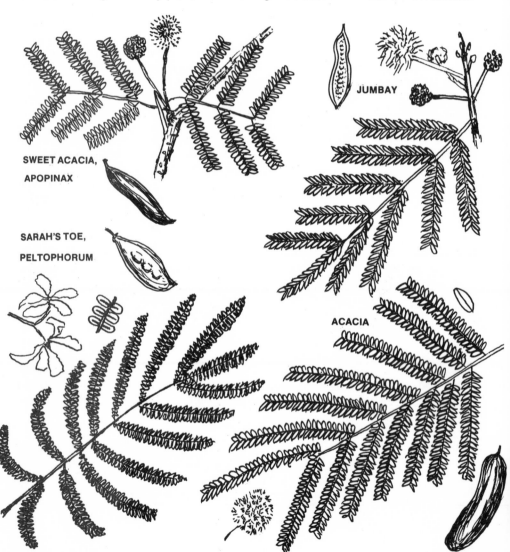

SWEET ACACIA   ACACIA FARNESIANA

10 - 15 feet. **TRUNK** slender to medium, sometimes with spines 1 - 2" long. **CROWN** wide and spreading; branches long, drooping, armed with spines 1" long or more, single or paired. **BARK** brown, thin, on old trees splitting into small pieces. **TWIGS** brown, zig-zag or curved, slightly roughened with lenticels; spines 1" or longer in leaf axils, single or paired. **LEAVES** alternate; leaflets very numerous; smooth, bright to dark green and dull above and below; 1/4" long or less. **FLOWERS** in spring or early summer, occasionally throughout the year; numerous, minute, in thick, showy, bright yellow heads about 1/2" across, on axillary stalks 1" long, very fragrant. **FRUIT** in summer, occasionally all year; narrow, flat brown pod 1 - 3" long, 1" wide. **FOUND** in Central Bahamas, generally in scrub or cut-over land. Florida, Jamaica, Cuba to Tobago, Central and South America, Old World tropics. Leguminosae.

JUMBAY   LEUCAENA LEUCOCEPHALA

10 - 20 feet. **TRUNK** slender, straight or crooked. **CROWN** irregular, sparse, narrow; branches erect. **BARK** brown, thin, somewhat roughened by numerous pale lenticels, slightly fissured on older trees. **TWIGS** brown, slender, usually straight, smooth, covered with numerous lenticels. **LEAVES** alternate; leaflets numerous; smooth, thin, dark green and dull above, paler below; 1/4 - 1/2" long; very narrow; tip pointed, base pointed. **FLOWERS** all year; very small, in dense, creamy-white round heads about 2/3" across, turning brown with age, on axillary stalks 1 - 2" long. **FRUIT** all year; dark brown, flat pod about 3/4" wide and 4 - 6" long. **FOUND** throughout the Bahamas, very common in cut-over land. Originally introduced as fodder for horses — but it makes their tails drop off. Bermuda, Florida, West Indies, New and Old World tropics. Leguminosae.

SARAH'S TOE   PELTOPHORUM ADNATUM

15 - 30 feet. **TRUNK** medium to thick, short. **CROWN** spreading, often regular, medium dense; branches numerous, erect. **BARK** gray-brown to dark brown, thick, rough, splitting into plates and fissures with age. **TWIGS** brown, slender to medium, straight or slightly curved, heavily marked with leaf scars; smooth, rust-brown, downy at the tips. **LEAVES** deciduous, alternate; leaflets numerous; smooth, firm, dark green and shiny above, paler below; midrib prominent; 1/8 - 1/3" long; tip and base rounded, turning brown when ready to fall. **FLOWERS** in early summer; numerous, very showy, bright yellow, about 1" across, on much branched terminal spike 4" long or more. **FRUIT** in summer; flat brown pod about 2" long and 1/3" wide. **FOUND** on South Andros, Exuma, and Long Island, not common. One of the most beautiful of the Bahamian trees, should be in every garden. Cuba. Leguminosae.

ACACIA   ACACIA MACRACANTHA

10 - 25 feet. **TRUNK** slender to medium, short, irregularly armed with spines, usually in pairs. **CROWN** spreading, irregular; branches erect, numerous. **BARK** gray, blotched, smooth; on close inspection, apparently striped. **TWIGS** gray-green, zig-zag, with raised lines and small white dots, often with slender spines in the leaf axils. **LEAVES** alternate; 10 - 20 pairs of leaflets; smooth, firm, dark green and dull above, paler below; about 1/8" long; tip and base rounded. **FLOWERS** in spring and early summer; very small, bright yellow, in dense globose heads 1/3" across, on slender axillary stalks 1/2 - 1" long. **FRUIT** in early summer; slender pods 3 - 5" long, green turning brown. **FOUND** on Inagua, within a limited area. Jamaica, Cuba irregularly to Venezuela. Leguminosae.

COMPOUND LEAVES   BRANCHING STEMS

K. Leaf with odd number of branching stems..Jacaranda

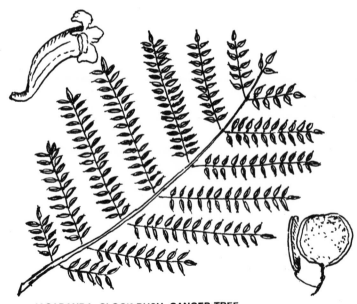

JACARANDA, CLOCK BUSH, CANCER TREE

10 - 30 feet. **TRUNK** slender to medium, straight. **CROWN** narrow, not dense; branches short, erect. **BARK** gray, thin and smooth on young trees, darker, thick, rough in vertical furrows with age. **TWIGS** green, slender, straight, smooth, with occasional lenticels. **LEAVES** opposite; 17 - 35 leaflets; thin, smooth, bright green and shiny above. paler below; midrib prominent; 1/2 - 3/4" long; stem 1/8" long or less; tip short pointed. blunt, or rounded, base wedge or unequal. **FLOWERS** throughout the summer; numerous. clustered, showy, blue-purple, about 1 1/2" long, on branched terminal stalk 3 - 7" long. **FRUIT** in winter and spring; about 2" long, round flat brown pod. **FOUND** in Central Bahamas, but not on San Salvador; common in mixed broadleaf areas, should be used more in landscaping. Cuba. Bignoniaceae.

Our knowledge of the plant species of the Bahamas is imperfect, though increasing. It must be accepted as a probability of high order that species of trees not previously known to be established in these islands will be discovered, and that other species once listed and now dropped will be re-instated. The species below are examples of each of these cases. Their presence in the Bahamas was verified just before this book went to press, and too late for inclusion in the main body of the work. Both are quire rare, and neither has been seen by the authors. For the data offered here, we are indebted to Dr. John Popenoe and Dr. Donovan S. Correll, both of Fairchild Tropical Garden, Miami, with some further detail on Rochefortia taken from Bahama Flora. by Britton and Millspaugh.

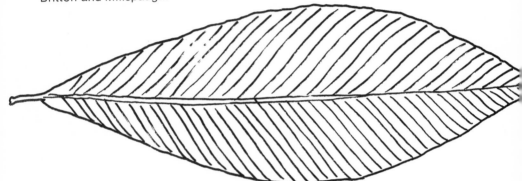

WALLENIA LAURIFOLIA

20 feet tall or less, an understory tree. **TRUNK** 4 - 6 inches in diameter. bark fairly smooth. **LEAVES** alternate, medium firm, bright shiny green above, dull green below: midrib prominent, concave on upper surface, raised on lower surface; veins numerous: about 6" long; stem 1/2", pale red; tip blunt pointed, base narrow. **FRUIT** a red berry. **FOUND** on Grand Bahama. Cuba, Hispaniola, Jamaica. Myrsinaceae.

ROCHEFORTIA SPINOSA

10 feet or less, more often a shrub. **TRUNK** slender, branches spreading. **BARK** scaly. **TWIGS** leathery, easily bent, gray-green, sometimes spined at the nodes. **LEAVES** leathery, dark green and dull above, somewhat lighter below; 3/4 - 1 1/2" long; stem 1/3" long or less; midrib conspicuous, veing few and not prominent; tip blunt or notched. base blunt or wedge. **FLOWERS** pale green, 1/4" long, in groups of 2 to 4 in the axils. **FRUIT** not described. **FOUND** in Southern Bahamas. Boraginaceae.

INTRODUCED SPECIES OFTEN FOUND IN WILD STATE

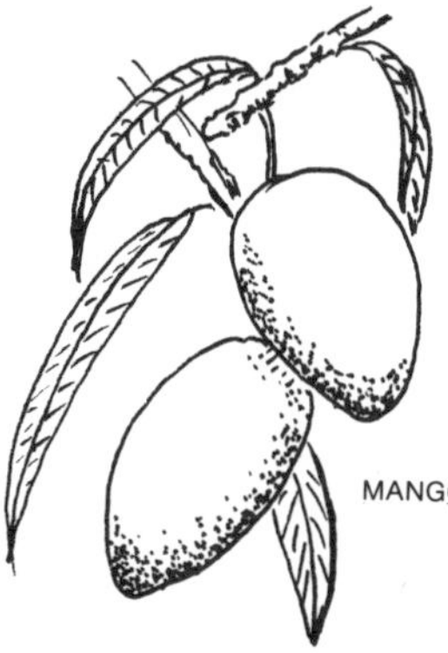

MANGO

YELLOW ELDER

AVOCADO

SUGAR APPLE

BRAZILIAN PEPPER

SOURSOP

GUAVA

WEST INDIAN ALMOND

EGGFRUIT

GENIP

MUNTINGIA

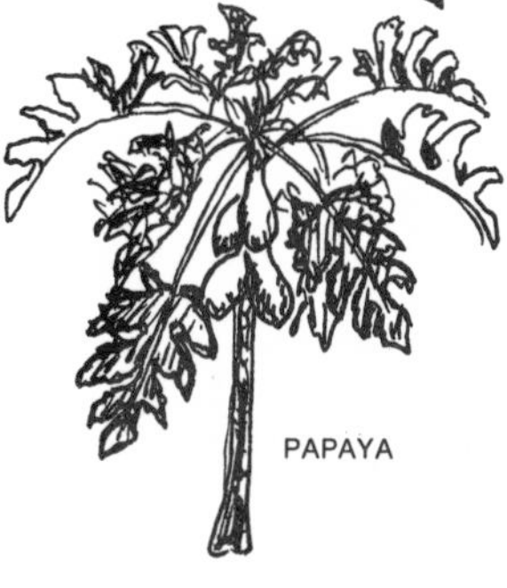

PAPAYA

SOME COMMON SHRUBS AND PLANTS

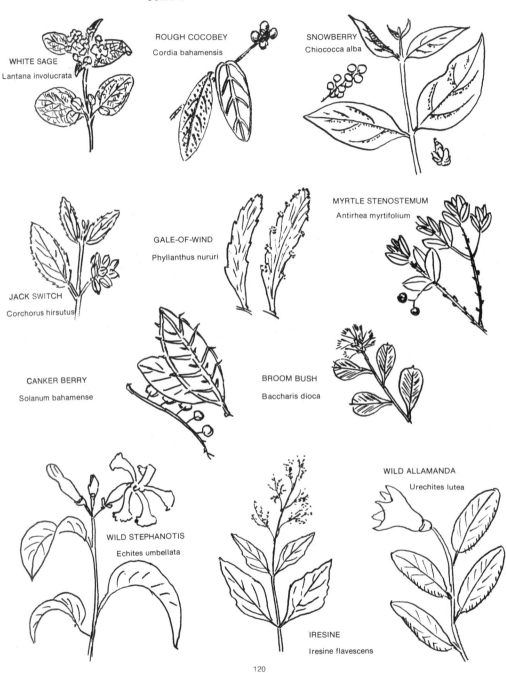

WHITE SAGE
Lantana involucrata

ROUGH COCOBEY
Cordia bahamensis

SNOWBERRY
Chiococca alba

JACK SWITCH
Corchorus hirsutus

GALE-OF-WIND
Phyllanthus nururi

MYRTLE STENOSTEMUM
Antirhea myrtifolium

CANKER BERRY
Solanum bahamense

BROOM BUSH
Baccharis dioca

WILD STEPHANOTIS
Echites umbellata

IRESINE
Iresine flavescens

WILD ALLAMANDA
Urechites lutea

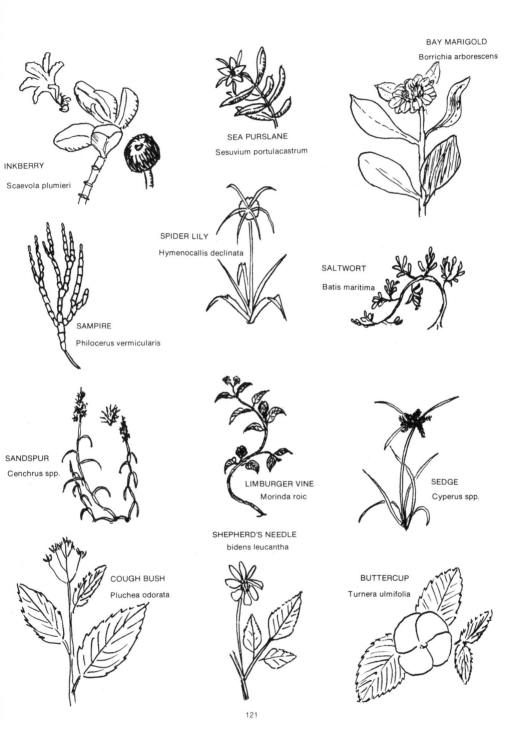

BAY MARIGOLD
Borrichia arborescens

SEA PURSLANE
Sesuvium portulacastrum

INKBERRY
Scaevola plumieri

SPIDER LILY
Hymenocallis declinata

SALTWORT
Batis maritima

SAMPIRE
Philocerus vermicularis

SANDSPUR
Cenchrus spp.

LIMBURGER VINE
Morinda roic

SEDGE
Cyperus spp.

SHEPHERD'S NEEDLE
bidens leucantha

COUGH BUSH
Pluchea odorata

BUTTERCUP
Turnera ulmifolia

121

DISTRIBUTION OF BAHAMIAN TREES

The following data are drawn from Bahama Flora, by Britton and Millspaugh, 1920. Botanical advances in the past 50 years may have increased the known ranges of some species, but in the main these lists are probably fairly accurate still. The species appear here in the order used in this book.

A few species are found in most tropical regions of the globe. These are Coconut, Casuarina, Mahoe, Cork Tree, Tallowwood, Red Mangrove, Coast Sophora, Sweet Acacia, and Jumbay.

Those that are found throughout the Caribbean Basin, including South Florida, are Royal Palm, Anaconda, Manchioneel, Salve Bush, Myrsine, Caper Tree, Cocoplum, Swamp Bush (Pavonia), Sea Grape, Buttonwood, Cassada Wood, Pond Apple, Sapodilla, Bay Cedar, Duranta, Steelwood, False Boxwood, Rough Leaf Velvet Seed, Black Torch, Princewood, Black Mangrove, White Mangrove, Mahogany, Dogwood, Gum-Elemi, Paradise Tree, Sweet Torch, Wild Lime, Cat's Claw. Velvet Bush, Wild Mamee, and Wild Oak (Bucida) belong in this group, but are not found in Florida.

The Bahamas share a number of species with South Florida and Cuba, and, in most cases, with one or more other Caribbean Islands. Hog Cabbage Palm, Pond Top Palm, Spanish Top Palm, Buffalo Top Palm, Silver Palm, Yellow Pine, Spiny Milk Berry, Olive Wood, Dahoon Holly, Crabwood, Bay Berry, Trema, Saffron, Common Snake Bark, Cuban Snake Bark, Cinnamon Bark, Wild Orange, Strong Back, Box Wood, Bahama Maidenbush, Pigeon Plum, Wild Fig, Short Leaf Wild Fig, Gulf Graytwig, Guiana Plum, Lancewood, White Wood, Krug's Holly, West Indian Laurel Cherry, Mastic, Wild Dilly, Soldier Wood, Marl Berry, Wild Cherry, Smooth Leaf Velvet Seed, Seven Year Apple, Guana Berry, Joewood, Blolly, Wild Guava (Tetrazygia), Fiddlewood, White Stopper, Red Stopper, Ironwood (Eugenia), Spicewood, Myrtle-of-the-River, Spanish Stopper, Swamp Bush (Forestiera), Pisonia, Darling Plum, Ironwood (Krugiodendron), Inkwood, Lignum Vitae, Hercules Club, White Ironwood, Snakeroot, Satin Wood, Poison Wood, Alvaradoa, Ram's Horn, and Wild Tamarind.

The Bahamas and Cuba, excluding Florida, have an impressive list in common. Most of these are also found on one or more of the other Caribbean Islands. Red Cedar, Soldier Berry, Cow Bush, Wild Salve, Tear Coat, Brier Tree, Mexican Plume Poppy, Cahoney, Candlewood, False Holly, Young Manchioneel, Cuban Holly, Smooth Casearia, Rat Wood, Polygala, Bull Wood, Swamp Bush (Dodonea), Box Wood, Pigeon Berry, Boar Pigeon Plum, Roughbark Pigeon Plum, Bastard Pigeon Plum, Small Leaf Wild Fig, White Beefwood, Bontia, Cestrum, Feather Bed, Frangipanni, Wild Guava (Catesbaea), Seersucker, Old Man, Hairy Wild Coffee, False Resin Leaf, Boar Mastic, Coppice Joewood, Fowl Berry, Resin Leaf, Rauwolfia, Parrot Wood, Quina, Beefwood, Naked Wood, Marigold, Chicken Toe, Two Leaf, Spanish Cedar, Mosquito Bush, Logwood, Three Leaf, Bitter Wood, Boar Gum-Elemi, Cuban Yellow Wood, Stinking Pea Root, Spathelia, Bahama Cat's Claw, Casinas, Horseflesh, Cinnecord, Brasiletto, Blue Seed, Sarah's Toe, Acacia Macracantha, Jacaranda. Pain-in-Back is not found in Cuba, but is present on many of the other islands and in Mexico.

Fifteen species are thought to be endemic, found only in the Bahamas and Caicos. These are Wild Okra Wild Hibiscus, Bahama Swamp Bush, Zizyphus, Wild Holly, Milk Berry, Sweet Wood Bark, Bahama Pigeon Plum, Touch-Me-Not, Neobracea, Milk Tree, Quicksilver Bush, Bahama Stopper, Bahama Haulback, and Pork and Doughboy.

DISTRIBUTION OF BAHAMIAN TREES

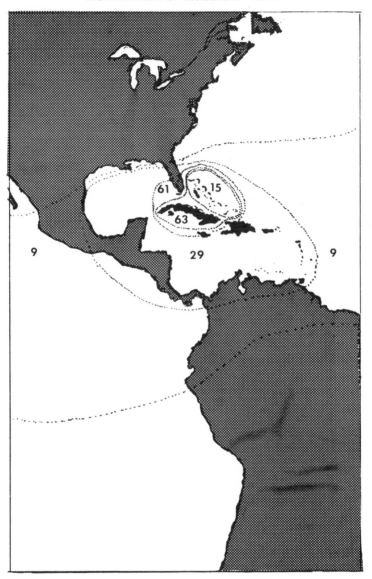

The species considered in this book are members of 53 families.

Anacardiaceae, 1 (104).
Annonaceae, 1 (50).
Apocynaceae, 3 (60, 66, 78).
Aquifoliaceae, 3 (24, 26, 50).
Bignoniaceae, 3 (90, 90, 116).
Boraginaceae, 3 (20, 30, 36).
Burseraceae, 2 (102, 104).
Buxaceae, 1 (80).
Canellaceae, 1 (32).
Capparidaceae, 1 (32, 32).
Casuarinaceae, 1 (12).
Celastraceae, 5 (26, 34, 38, 64, 64).
Combretaceae, 4 (18, 44, 60, 90).
Compositae, 1 (22).
Dodonaceae, 1 (36).
Ebenaceae, 1 (54).
Erythroxylaceae, 3 (34, 36, 54).
Euphoribiaceae, 13 (18, 22, 24, 24, 26, 26, 28, 34, 36, 46, 50, 50, 56).
Flacourtiaceae, 3 (22, 22, 24).
Guttiferae, 1 (70).
Lauraceae, 2 (48, 48).
Leguminosae, 21 (96, 96, 102, 104, 106, 108, 108, 108, 108, 110, 110, 110, 110, 112, 112, 112, 112, 114, 114, 114, 114).
Malpighiaceae, 3 (66, 70, 78).
Malvaceae 7 (14, 14, 14, 14, 16, 16, 18).
Melastomaceae, 1 (76).
Meliaceae, 2 (94, 94).
Moraceae, 3 (44, 44, 44).
Myoporaceae, 1 (46).
Myricaceae, 1 (24).
Myrsinaceae, 2 (32, 56).
Myrtaceae, 8 (80, 80, 80, 84, 84, 84, 86, 88).
Nyctaginaceae, 3 (74, 86, 90).
Olacaceae, 3 (20, 46, 46).
Oleaceae, 2 (70, 88).
Palmae, 7 (8, 8, 8, 10, 10, 10, 10).
Papaveraceae, 1 (20)
Picrodendraceae, 1 (98).
Pinaceae, 2 (12, 12).
Polygalaceae, 1 (36).
Polygonaceae, 6 (40, 40, 42, 42, 42, 42).
Rhamnaceae, 6 (18, 30, 30, 56, 92, 92).
Rhizophoraceae, 1 (82).
Rosaceae, 2 (36, 52).
Rubiaceae, 11 (62, 62, 66, 68, 68, 68, 70, 72, 74, 78, 78).
Rutaceae, 7 (94, 96, 98, 100, 102, 104, 106).
Sapindaceae, 4 (94, 98, 100, 100).
Sapotaceae, 7 (20, 30, 34, 48, 52, 52, 54).
Simaroubaceae, 4 (60, 102, 106, 106).

Solanaceae, 2 (30, 48).
Sterculiaceae, 3 (16, 16, 28).
Theophrastaceae, 2 (72, 72).
Ulmaceae, 1 (28).
Verbenaceae, 6 (62, 64, 76, 76, 76, 88).
Zygophyllaceae, 1 (96).

INDEX OF COMMON NAMES

INDEX OF BOTANICAL NAMES